Tales

of the

Chuck Wagon

By
N. H. (Jack) Thorp

Author of
Songs of the Cowboys
Houghton Mifflin & Co., Publ's.

To Tom Doran
A. Adamson
and the thousands of other
old cow-hands of the West
this little book is inscribed

INDEX

Tales of the Chuck Wagon

FOREWORD

During the yearly round-up on the Closed-H range, we usually worked some ten cow-hands, with a daily average of fifteen stray men representing other cow outfits who had cattle on our range.

These stray men would meet the Closed-H punchers once or twice a year on the "works", or round-ups, and at those meetings they would bring news from many and distant points. In the days of few railroads and no telephones, about the only way of transmitting news was through the punchers going from one outfit to another.

It had been an old established custom with the Closed-H outfit that the men working on the round-up should meet on the first night at the chuck-wagon—i. e., the grub-wagon. Every man there was obliged either to tell a story, sing a song, or do a dance. Anyone refusing was sure to get a dose of the leggings, a punishment administered by the other punchers, several of whom would grab the offender and stretch him, toes and face down, across the wagon-tongue, while another puncher applied the leather leggings or chaps. Such treatment, you can be sure, usually elicited a response in the form of song, story, or dance.

This little collection is composed, for the most part, of yarns told by cow-punchers who worked at various times with the Closed-H wagon.

N. H. T.

OLD-MAN RIVERS FINDS RELIGION

It had been raining hard all day, and as we couldn't do anything else we were just settin around the wagon under a bed-tarp which we'd streched from the bows to some pegs driven into the ground. It was mighty damp. The boys who were on day-herd were riden round in slickers and cussin' the wet country. Not that you could call it natcherally wet, 'cause it never rains over five or six days in the year in that part of New Mexico, and then altogether in the month of June. I say we were settin' there feelin' kind o' dull when up rides Jess Hill from the Sacramentos driven' a mount of horses who'd come over to represent the Y-O- outfit, they havin' a few cattle scattered on our range. Jess was one of the tallest punchers I've ever seen, a good hand, and always likin' to play off a joke on someone when he had a chance. After he'd hobbled his mount of horses and thrown his bedroll under our tarpaulin he sat down and commenced to roll him a smoke.

"How did you come in?" I asked.

"Over the Chilicoot Pass", he replied, which was a name we had given a steep trail entering the Sacramento River, "and it's sure slick, and the bottoms are plenty boggy. I had my pack-horse down twice, and the last time like te'r never got him out. Punchin' cows in these mountains ain't like it is in a book I read before I left the ranch, where all the cute Waddie had ter do was ride slick fat horses, sleep on a geese-hair bed, set the boss' daughter en afterwards marry her, en she the prettiest girl in the

West. I wonder why some sure-enough cow hand don't write the truth about it, heh?''

"Well, Jess I guess those fellows that write those books figure it out this way.

"If we feelers that were raised in a saddle would a' wrote those books we wouldn't a' been raised in the saddle, and those fellers who do write the books haven't been raised in the saddle, and that's the reason they can write 'em. They was raised in an office. En say, Jess wouldn't you and I look fine settin' here under this bed-sheet tryin' to write a story about one of them offices in a big city, huh?

"Yeah" says Jess, "that book started tellin' about a feller who was a-drivin' a bunch of saddle-horses into a corral off the open range, en mind yer this was the last er April before any green grass was up, en he says the horses was hog fat and shed off, en the same chapter a little farther on he says the boss had lost thousands er cattle the last two years because it hadn't rained. Wouldn't it make you sick, huh?''

"Say Jess, yer been over to Chimney Lake lately?''

"Yeah.''

"Still settin' old-man Rivers' girl, are yer?''

"Nope.''

"What's the trouble?''

"Nothing much—only she's got married.''

"Who to?''

"Old Skeeter Mayes.''

"Is that so?''

"Yes, that's so, en she didn't get much when she married him either."

"Say, does the old man still cuss es much es ever?"

"No, he's done quit."

"How so?"

"Got him religion."

"Got him religion?"

"Yep; it was this a-way. Yer remember old-lady Truesdale from over at Weed?"

"Yeah."

"Well, yer know she was always strong on religion, en last year she goes to her old home in Texas en happened down there when their cotton crops were all in en they'd jes' started the camp meetings, and I guess from what she says she must'a been to every one in Texas; jest seems she got her religion all shined up. When she got back that was all she could talk about—it was what Brother So-en-so en what Sister So-en-so said en done, en how she was baptised. She said when they called for converts she was so excited she jest marched up with the bunch en they shoved her under, head en all; en it was never till late the next day that she remembered she had already been baptised, more than thirty years before. Well, she and old-lady Rivers had always been great friends from before they left Texas en had a sort er mutual interest in having a Revivalist come out en hold a meetin'. So before old-lady Truesdale came back she arranged for a cousin of hers who was one of the best converters in Texas to come en hold a set of revivals on the Penasco River. All the people who come from where the Truesdales come from always said that it was only because the old man happened ter be a little earlier riser than the sheriff en rode a better horse he wasn't hung when he left Texas. En because old-man Rivers was so strong on cussin' en the bottle en so short on doin' any work, was the reason them two women who'd drawn blanks took such en interest in seein' em get converted. Old-man Rivers and I always used ter get along fine en he as much as told me I'd suit him fer a son-in-law. But that was before the time when he killed the two deer standin' side by side on a bluff with my saddle gun at one shot, or at least he said he did en I wouldn't believe it, that's when he divorced me. Well it wasn't long after old-lady Truesdale's return when sure enough the Preacher arrived and all the women folks were doin their best to entertain him. They were a-drivin him up and down the river ter see which place he would choose ter hold the revival meetings at. I knew they was bound ter be some hard feelin's over it en sure enough there was. Old woman Cox said Mrs. Ward's husband had stolen his start in cattle en she needn't put on any airs. Mrs. Ward said that before the Coxes left Texas that they were in the store business, en burned out twice to collect the insurance. Well, about then the Preacher decided not to have the doings on anyone's ranch, end at a meetin' he called, explained that the men could take their teams en wagons en cut cedar en build him a big arbour, en Collins, who ran the saw-mill, said he would subscribe the lumber fer the floor en benches. Well, exceptin' the time when they had the Rodeo at Roswell I never saw so many people together before. There was Ty Jones, en you know he has served two terms fer cow-stealin', a-settin up there by his wife a-holdin' a baby, en when the Preacher got'em all het up en called fer the sinners ter come confess and repent, Ty was in such a hurry he started down the aisle to the mourners' bench luggin' the kid with him, stumbled over someone's hat in the aisle, dropped the little old baby en never even stopped ter pick it up. Then old-man Bland en Coey Combs that run the Rattlesnake saloon at Weed up en promised never to open up 'en they was both plum sober.' Then Rank Thomas the gambler said he'd never turn another card, en all the cow-punchers stacked their six-shooters on the altar en said they was through. Old-man Cabot, who'd shot the ear off of Gay Thurman the year before, when the boys had put them on day-herd together, was a holdin' each other's hands en sayin' how sorry they was, en old Truesdale en Rivers was dipped, bathed, en had all their sins washed away at one time. Everybody who had confessed said they felt so good that they wanted every one else to do the same, en they was a sister'n en a brother'n each other till I was plum disgusted en went on home.

"Well, it was some three weeks after that first meetin' that I was over near Chimney Lake, me and Bill Mug bein' over there on a hunt fer some saddle horses that had strayed off, when we meets up with old-man Rivers comin' from Weed ter his home. Well I guess the new religion made him feel so good t'wards his fellow man that he made us go over en spend the night. Ma Rivers en the girl seemed just tickled ter death ter see us—this was before she married Skeeter Mayes—en made us put up our horses en come right in, Ma Rivers all the while talkin' about the great change that hed come over Pa since he'd got him religion, en how industrious he'd become, en how he'd quit swearin' en everything. Letty, that's the girl's name, yer know, began playin' the parlor organ, Ma a-cookin' supper, en Pa a-pullin' on his old pipe like a team er horses.

"Jest es we were about ter set down, up rides a couple er punchers and sez they was ridin' fer the Double Diamonds, en es their saddle-horses was in that brand I guess they was. One was some fifteen hands high en the other a sure enough Shetland. Well, Ma Rivers sets me down at the end of the table next ter Pa, who d'rectly bows his head en begins ter talk ter the food. Seems they didn't ask no ordianry blessin' but each member of the family, before they washed their faces in the morning learned a new verse out of the Bible en spilled it out jest before they begin eatin'. Pa gets rid er his learnin' then the girl says her little piece then Bill Mug stutters somethin', en me too, Ma likewise, en it come aroun' ter the biggest er the Double Diamond waddies, who up en tossed out the shortes' verse they tell me's in the Bible, jest plain Jesus wept. The little Shetland who was settin' next ter him was up a tree fer sure. He wasn't raised where any Bible Societies was in the habit ev' slippin' one in yer saddle pocket before each round-up. He looks around the table, then under it then at old high-boy, his partner, en at last spits his out—He sure did, says he, thinkin' all the time ev the verse his partner had said en feelin' he ought ter back him up.

"Presently, that bein' over, we had a sure enough good meal with some sugared melon ter end up with. Well I guess we was at the table some half-hour when Pa after huntin' up his pipe, began fillen' her with homespun en all the time tellin' Bill Mug en me what a heap er good the Preacher had done ter all the folks down the creek, en how drinken' en swearen was jest the devil croppen out in 'us, and they weren't any sense in it anyway, en he had never known anyone who did those things ter get any benefit from 'em en about then we all gets up from the table. The old man had a habit er goin' over ter the fire place en picken' up a live coal en lighten his pipe, en from havin' worked the best part of his life, when he would work, in the mines, his hands were tough, en he would most always get a light before he had ter drop the coal.

"Bill Mug was a standen looken out er the window as the old man started fer the fireplace, but keepin' him covered with one eye. Jest as Rivers picks up er red hot coal Bill lets out a squawk, en pointen out er the windor hollers: 'Look at the deer, get yer gun.'

"The old man with the hot coal still between his

fingers, runs ter look, en by the time he got there the coal had jest about sizzled through the hide.

"Hell-fire and danbation: shouts the old man, droppen the coal en he kept on a-cussin' en a-cussin'.

" 'Pa, Pa,' sings out the old woman, 'yer ought ter be ashamed er yerself 'goin' en losin' all yer religion. But I don't know as it was entirely yer fault, fer I do believe those boys hev done it a-purpose.' En I ain't been back since," concludes Jess Hill.

And the rest of us cow-punchers laughed till you couldn't a herd the rain beatin' down on the wagon tarpaulin over our heads.

THE LOST NAVAJOS

I was settin' on top o' the horse corral gate a-gazin' out across the flats, when I notice somethin' a-kickin' up the dust in the direction o' Wolf Mountain. By the time I'd twisted en finished the first smoke I made out there was a saddle horse a-comin', en a pack-horse bein' led. After I'd had my second smoke, who should ride up out o' the dust but Buster.

"Hello, Buster, get down. Where'd you come from?"

"Over in the basin."

"Tonto?"

"Yep, workin' fer the Mule Shoes. Told me to come over en ride with you boys durin' the work."

"Well, sure glad to have yer. We're awful short handed. Turn your horses into the *remuda;* chuck's jest about ready. We've finished the horse work en no guard to stand tonight, so yer can tell us what hell you been raisin' since we saw yer last."

"Well, I've been workin' for a sheep outfit."

"Sheep!"

"Yep."

"What doin'?"

"Huntin' the boss."

"Did yer find him?"

"Nope."

"How long were yer workin'?"

"Six months."

"Workin' fer a man six months en yer didn't find him?"

"Yep, it was this-a-way. I'd quit the Lazy-B outfit en pulled over to Young's to rest a few days en sets in a poker game at Al Hamblin's place, but somehow there weren't spots enough on the cards I held, en I was jest a-mind to quit when in walks a Mexican dressed like a sheep-herder, en I hear him ask the bar-keep if Mr. Holspeill was in the house, en the bar-keep sent him over to the table where I was tryin' to get a hand. When he come over he touched the man who was sittin' next to me on the shoulder, en says he, 'Senor Holspeill, I want to talk some to you.'

"So this man Holspeill cashes in en they goes over to a bench en sits down. Well, I tries fer some time to get somethin' higher than a two-spot, en as she wouldn't come I cashes in en quits, twenty-four bones to the bad. As I starts out o' the door this gent Holspeill speaks to me, en says he, 'Do yer know where I can get a man that knows the country over east o' here on the line o' the Navajo?'

" 'Yes,' says I, 'I know jest the man. What kind o' work is it, en what's in it?'

" 'Well,' says he, 'my sheep boss has quit the flock, it seems, from what this man tells me, without no reason, en can't be found, en I want a man to take his trail en find him.'

" 'Well, I know that country, en if you'll pay what it's worth I'll go over en try to locate him fer yer.'

"As we don't have no trouble gettin' together on the price en outfit question, I asks him what he knows about his lost sheep boss. He tells me he's a Scotch-man, tall en with sandy-colored hair, en his name is Dan MacLaw; had been with him a year or so en was a fine sheep man, en liked to play what's called a bag-pipe, which together with his crazy colored Scotch clothes, he always carried with him wherever he went.

"Well, the next mornin' Mr. Mex, or Juanito as they called him, en I, pulled out. Say, do yer know that country?"

"Nope."

'Well, after yer get out o' the basin it's all high mesas, en goin' by Jack's Mountain that night we pulled into Cherry Creek. Next day at noon, Cañon Creek, en that night we gets to Cibicue, en Juanito tells me if we have good luck in three or four days more we'll get to where the lost man was last seen.

"Let me tell yer, I always thought that gray horse o' mine was pretty good, but a week after we left, en when we pulled into Sunrise, alongside o' that little Mexican mule Juanito rode, he wouldn't cast a shadow.

"We stops all night at a sheep camp, en me en the Mexican got filled up on tortillas en mutton a-plenty. Next mornin' I rides over to the town o' Sunrise where MacLaw had last been seen, fer all I could get out of Juanito was, 'He go, I no see more.'

"There was only one store of any size there, so I ties my horse en ambles in, wonderin' how MacLaw got out o' that country without a horse en saddle, as his were still at the sheep camp. I meets up with the feller who owns the tradin' post, en I want to say right now, he was full o' information en not afraid to pass it along. After I told him my business he begun to laugh and insteal o' gettin' mad I laughs with him. I been in lots of queer jack-pots en on lots o' fool errands in my life, but never one that seemed as queer as this, fer I've heard of a boss losin' herds o' sheep lots o' time, but I never before heard of a bunch o' sheep losin' their boss.

"Well, at last he spits her out: ' 'Twas this way: 'bout a month ago was the Navajo fire dance, en that same day the boss's sheep come in from the north, several flocks of 'em, en watered there at the creek jest in front o' the store, then drifted on down the cañon. Pretty soon up drives the chuck-wagon en this feller I guess ye're lookin' fer. Dan was his name, wasn't it?'

"Yep," says I.

" 'Well, the wagon stops, en him en the Mexican who was drivin' the chuck-wagon comes in. He tells me he's sheep boss fer old man Holspeill, en as I'se known the old man always I tells him he can have anythin' he wants, so he stocks up with a lot o' grub fer the camp en grain fer the horses.

" 'While the boys was loadin' the wagon, in comes old Tony who lives up the creek en who used to work fer this Dan, as I learned afterwards. Well, Tony had a bottle of this Navajo Tis-win, en him en Dan had several drinks en commenced to tell each other how much they thought of each other, en Tony

tells Dan that the Navajos are goin' to have a fire
dance that night, en fer Dan to let the wagon man
make camp below town, en fer Dan to go over to *his*
house for the night.

" 'Well, that seemed ter jest suit Dan, as he explained he never had seen an Indian dance before.

" 'So gettin' his grip out o' the wagon he tells
his driver to go a mile or two below town where the
grass was good, en make camp; to tie his saddle horse
behind, en he'd be down in the mornin'.

" 'Well, there was all kind o' Pueblo Indians
there en some Apaches and Utes, with a big swarm
o' Navajos, all camped up and down the creek.
They'd been gamblin', drinkin', en runnin' horse
races fer several days. They had a big cedar corral
built, en hauled stacks o' wood en piled it up in the
middle all ready to light when night come on.

" 'I had a big run o' trade that evenin', and did-
n't see no more o' Dan, but I saw Tony several times
makin' trips across to the board shack fer Tis-win,
en guessed he en Dan was havin' a-plenty.

" 'About ten o'clock that night the Navvies began dacin', en you could hear the big drums en singin' fer miles. So, as everybody had gone to the
dance, en my tradin' fer the day was over, me en one
o' the boys who works in the store thought we'd go
too. They'd jest got to that point in the fire dance
where they're all trottin' around the fire with nothin' on but a cotton breech-clout en everyone pokin'
the man ahead of him with a lighted torch, when we

heard the worst noise yer ever heard in your life. No
one knew what it was—sounded as if you had a
mountain lion in a sack en was chokin' it to death.

" 'Then out o' the dark into the light o' the big
fire, came your man Dan. He had a little short skirt
to his knees, bare legs, a pair o' low shoes, a funny
little cap with a long feather in it of all colors of the
rainbow, drunk as a lord en blowin' on some kind of
an instrument (yes, that was what Holspeill told me
he called a bag-pipe) en a'makin' an awful racket.
Well, sir ,the Indians didn't know what to make of
it; I overheard some of 'em speakin' in Navajo (you
know I understand it), askin' each other what tribe
he belonged to. One would say Omaha, another Ogal-
lala, another Sioux. But anyway a Navajo is a good
sport, en whenever they find another man who can
out-dress 'em or can make more ungodly sounds en
call it music, they will follow him to the ends o' the
world.

" 'Well, Dan with his bag-pipe en enormous load
marched solemnly through the brush corral en out
again into the darkness, the band o' Navvies followin' in line behind him, en where they went, young
man, is fer you ter find out. But one thing is certain,
from that day to this, neither Dan nor that bunch o'
Navvies has ever been heard of.' "

YOUNG DE VARGAS

"Come on, Skeeter," said the foreman of the Closed-H, "quit pullin' on that pill en come through. Yer haven't let a yap out o' yer since yer come. What's new over your way, en what yer been doin' since we saw yer last?"

"Nothin' much," replied Skeeter, who had ridden from the Salt-creek country to represent the S-L-Y outfit. I was up in Santa Fé last year, en that old town sure has grown. Instead o' puttin' up Christian wooden houses fer the people to live in, all the rich folks are buildin' common old adobes, just *chile*-pickers' houses. They're sure makin' a bid fer a crop o' centipedes en bedbugs.

"Yer see lots more Americans up there than yer used to, en most every one o' them can speak English. The week I was there the town was jest full o' strangers, tourists I guess they were, en when Lem Ryan and me struck town, it had so changed en was so jam full o' people we didn't know where to go. We jest stood on one o' the corners o' the *plaza* en tried to make ourselves as thin as we could to let the people get by. Presently some priests passed carryin' something, then a lot o' little girls dressed up in white, en still the people kept driftin' by us, thousands of 'em, en all headed in the same direction.

"I don't know where they all came from, but they was hours in passin'. I says to Lem, 'Lem! where do yer reckon all these folks are a-goin'? They are all headed in one direction.'

" 'Don't know fer sure,' says he, 'but think

they must be goin' to water.'

"En it wasn't until the next day we found out it was the De Vargas parade we had been lookin' at.

"Well, you boys might remember the time a few years ago when Dan Hall en I had a little misunderstandin'? Yes, I remember some o' you was at the funeral. Well, yer know he had some kin-folks back in Illinois, awful queer people who somehow didn't exactly understand those things, en who tried to make some trouble over it fer me. Well, who should I meet walkin' right across the Plaza but the very lawyer who defended me at the time. I introduced Lem to him en he was sure glad to see us. As we was leavin' him, Lem asked how far it was out to Tesuque as he had a brother livin' there en we thought we'd go out en see him. My lawyer friend said, 'Boys, these hacks here will rob you. If you will be ready to go in an hour I will phone my wife en ask her if she hasn't room in her automobile to take you out. How would that suit you?'

" 'Fine,' we both says at once, fer neither of us had ever ridden in an automobile before. My lawyer friend, as we afterwards found out, owned the largest car in town. As we was goin' to ride with a lady we got a shave, hair cut, en shine, en then moseyed over to the northeast corner o' the plaza where my friend's Missus was to meet us. At exackly two o'clock the automobile turned the corner en stopped.

"A man was drivin' it en a woman was settin' in the back seat. The driver was a young feller who must a been told not to say a word, fer that's what he spent all his time a-doin'. Say, if they paid a premium fer a man keepin' still, that feller in a year would a been rich.

"The lady smiled at us en asked if we was Mr. Skeeter en Mr. Ryan, en as we said we were en could prove it if necessary, she opened the door en we slipped into the back seat beside her. Say, that was a sure-enough swell car, brass everywhere en leather cushions that smelled like a new pair o' John Roker's shop-made boots.

"En she was some glider. We no sooner put our foot on board when she was gone. En bridle wise, en start, en stop just like a top-cuttin' horse! They called it six miles out to Lem Ryan's brother's ranch, en I jest had time to roll a smoke but not light it, when we was there.

"Well, when we stepped out o' the car, the lady tells us she has to go on a few miles further to the Indian Pueblo en will stop for us in about an hour. Say, that was the longest hour I ever spent. We ushers ourselves into one o' the best-staged family rough-houses it's ever been my luck to referee. We opens the gate, proceeds to the house en enters.

Lem's brother was Irish, en his wife too. Each had had another pardner before this marriage, en owned a boy apiece, of one and the same age. It seems her boy Dan had hit his boy Mike over the head with a bottle, en the old man was busy givin' Dan a good lickin', when the wife, not knowin' what had happened, suddenly appears from the garden, en she en her old man went to the floor about it.

"Well, I was in San Francisco the time o' the earthquake en fire, but that town looked like a model, 'longside the inside o' Ryan's home by the time the automobile got back. We never had a chance to say how-do-yer-do all the time we were there, fer they was so busy that they never even noticed when we came away.

"Well, Lem en me stepped in the car en we started back. Soon we began pullin' up a long hill, en the lady, seein' a Indian ahead walkin' in the direction we was goin', told the driver to ask him if he didn't want a ride. The driver when he caught up to him stopped the car, en speakin' to him in Spanish asked him to get in, which the Indian did, settin' himself next to the driver. The lady says to Lem and me, 'I suppose this is a great treat to this Indian ridin' in an automobile. Poor things, they never see anything or get to go anywhere. I always feel so sorry fer 'em. It seems hardly fair that things are so unequally divided in this world between the rich en poor. This Indian sure will tell his relatives about this treat, en look back on it in years to come.'

"Then leanin' forwards she told the driver to ask the Indian how he liked ridin' in a automobile.

" '*Bueno*,' replied the Indian.

" 'Ask him,' the lady said to the driver, 'if he has ever before ridden in one?'

" 'Si,' said the Indian.

" 'Why? Where?' asked the lady.

" Oh,' replies the Indian in perfectly good American, 'Chicago, New York, Paris, London, Berlin, Moscow, en St. Petersburg, en in most all the big cities. You see I was chief o' scouts fer Buffalo Bill's Wild West Show, durin' a two-year tour o' the world.'

"About then the auto pulls up at the *plaza,* en thankin' the lady we got out. Someone who knew her well told Lem that the lady of the automobile never had been out o' New Mexico in her life.

" 'Ugh!' says I.

"I suggests to Lem—on account of the poor Indian—that we take one. We done so. Presently we paces down the street in the direction the crowd is goin', en comes to a big curious shop.

" 'This was the place I was told to go when I came to this man's town, to get hair-quoits,' says Lem.

"Well, we walks in en meets a little short feller who says he was Mr. Candlesticks, but Lem en I never could remember afterwards if he told us he was the oldest curious man that ever owned a store, or the man that owned the oldest curious store. Anyway there was more junk in that place, en more curious-lookin' people walkin' around gettin' their noses into things en askin' fool questions, than a-plenty.

"Say, did yer ever see any o' them jumpin' beans?"

"Nope."

"Well, old Candlesticks had 'em. Yer see, they

jump off the counter when yer tickle 'em, en the old
man had a little Chihuahua dog to go and bring 'em
back again. We were lookin' at the things when in
comes some people, looked as if they was raised on
the Brooklyn Bridge. They knew a whole lot more
about Indians, from their talk, than old Candlesticks did, who had been tradin' with 'em all his life.
There was four o' them in the bunch. First to come
was a little dried-up old feller, en I guess the woman
with him was his wife, 'cause she was twice his size.
Another old girl follered, who Lem said made him
think of an old chuck-wagon-mule he used to work.
The last was a real swell-lookin' girl, en the funny
thing about her was she seemed to know it.

"Well, the big wife asks old Candlesticks one
fool question after another about blankets. What
was Balleta cloth? Did he have any, en could she
see it?

"She could, en the oldest curious dealer in the
world told her all about it. Seems, from what we
could overhear, the Navajo Indians used to come in
a couple hundred miles from their reservation en pay
old Candlesticks a dollar en a half a yard, (which
weighed a half a pound) fer this Balleta cloth. The
warrior would take it back home en give it to Mrs.
Navajo who would tear it apart en weave it into a
blanket. At the next new moon Mr. Navajo would
come back en sell the blanket to Mr. Candlesticks fer
fifty cents a pound.

"Well, after learnin' a whole lot about blanket makin', the lady that looked like a mule picked up

a skull, a real pretty one, clean and shiny, the kind the Indians on the reservation used to cut in two to stew their beans in. Well, old Mrs. Mule, who I guess had been readin' about Indians from books written in the funny-room of a New York paper before she came west, asked old Candlesticks if he knew whose skull it was.

" 'Turn it over, ladies, en you will see the owner's name,' says he, en sure enough there was a piece o' paper pasted over the bald spot with the name *De Vargas* printed on it. Well, of all the surprised women—to think that they was ackcherly holdin' the skull o' the great conqueror in their hands!

"After their pawin' it over fer some time, the little meek husband asks if he could look at it, en pullin' a glass from his pocket, began gazin'. Well, he takes a good look en says, 'Mr. Candlesticks, yer say this is the skull o' the great De Vargas?'

" 'Yes,' replied old Candlesticks, 'I pledge yer my reputation as a somethin' or other' (I didn't catch what) 'on it.'

" 'Well, Mr. Candlesticks," says the little feller, handin' him his card, 'I, as yer can see, am a surgeon en professor o' bones, etc., in the B. R. T. O. X. Y. College, en this skull is one of a male child probably eight years old.'

" 'Right you are,' replied the oldest curious man that ever owned a store, 'that is De Vargas's skull when he was a boy.'

" 'By heck,' says Lem, as we eased up the street towards the Call Again Saloon, 'cow-punchers ain't the only liars in the West after all.' "

WAGON WHEELS

"Hello, Hank, get down," hailed Johnson the foreman. "Been sick? Look as if you'd lost fifty pounds."

"No, I ain't sick," replied Hank. "Just got back from the chills and fever country."

"Been visiting?"

"Say I had; been to see the home folks back in Oklahoma, en I'm chuck full o' chills en fever, barbecued beef, en buffalo."

"Buffalo?"

"Yep, they sure fed us a-plenty of it."

"What part of Oklahoma was you at?"

"Down at Bliss. That's the old 1-0-1 Ranch headquarters, was down there for the reunion."

"Whose?"

"The C. S. C. P. A."

"Say her louder, Hank."

"Well, that means, if you're so ignorant, the Cherokee Strip Cow-puncher's Association."

"En, boys this Carrizozo flat is jest a mountainous cliff alongside o' Bliss. It's so level down there that the moon always comes up before ever the sun has a chance ter set. So flat you can see a cow comin' in to water before it leaves the tall grass, ten miles away, en the water in a forty-foot well a hundred miles off.

"Every Indian down there gets a check before breakfast each mornin' fer eighteen hundred dollars, en payment fer royalties on his oil well fer the day before. They ride in million-dollar autos en hire white men fer drivers. When I stepped off the train, there was a committee to meet me, en they sure were sociable en gave me a real Oklahoma breakfast.''

''What was that?'' inquired Johnson.

''Well, there was a band o' music walkin' ahead as they took me over to the hotel ter eat, where they gave me a sure-enough Oklahoma breakfast.''

''What of?'' asked Johnson.

''A bottle o' whiskey, some bologna sausage, en a dog.''

''A dog? What was the dog fer?'' asked Johnson.

''Oh,'' replied Hank, ''he was to eat up the sausages.''

''Well, how about the buffalo you was a-tellin' about?'' asked Johnson.

''Oh,'' says Hank, ''it was from a gentle herd the Miller Brothers kept on the ranch. One day they turned the herd lose in the middle of the park, en a bunch o' Indians a-horseback took after 'em, en those buffalo sure could hoof it. After the Indians had run the buffalo a while they killed a fat one, en the niggers that was doin' the cookin' at the re-union barbecued the meat to a good-bye.

''Durin' the day time, the 1-0-1 Ranch pulled off all the usual stunts you see at a rodeo, riding, roping, bull-doggin', en everything. Then there was a girl called Princess Winona (en she sure was some Princess) who did a lot o' fancy shootin' off her calico pony.

"Camped around the grounds was all the civilized en uncivilized tribes, eatin' pop-corn en drinkin' pop, jest as war-like as they could be. Ene old-timer was there that I was glad to see, old Pickett the darkey bull-dogger. He was the first man to introduce bull-doggin', en everyone gave him the glad hand."

"How was the ropin' en ridin?" asked Johnson.

"Jest regular," says Hank, "nothing much to brag about. Most o' the ropers en riders were civilized Indian boys, en as hands they'll never set the world a-fire.

"Well, in the evenin' the members of the C. S. C. P. A. got together under a big arbour made of boughs of trees, en had supper. Then the fun began. Every one had to either tell a story or sing. As most every member was fifty years old or older, the ones who tried ter sing had either lost their voices years before quetin' cattle, or strained 'em explainin' to different judges how they come to have their brands on some one else's cow. En the fellers who was asked to tell stories was either too bashful ter speak before such a crowd, or had forgotten what they wanted to say."

"Did they call on you?" asked Johnson.

"Sure did," replied Hank, "I told 'em, as usual, the truth. As they didn't believe me, when they asked for more talk I told 'em a plain lie, en they believed that all O. K.

"Then they called on a big feller, but he was so

bashful that he asked to be excused. The little feller who was a sittin' beside him ups and says that, as he came to the re-union with Fatty, en feelin' kind o' responsible fer him, he would try en make good fer his friend by tellin' how he first came to Oklahoma. So Ike Clubb (that was the little feller's name) told how, years before, he went over into Arkansas to buy cattle, as they were cheap over there in those days.

"They started out early one spring with a regular chuck-wagon en bunch of saddle horses. They crossed Oklahoma, then the big river, en landed in Arkansas where they grew hill-billies en swamp-angels. After a while the outfit got out o' the swamp lands en into the hills of the Black Mountain country, en everywhere they went, Ike said, they created a good deal of excitement. In those days every one livin' in Arkansas either traveled a-foot, or horseback, or in a two-wheel cart, as they said they could more easily dodge stumps travelin' that-a-way.

"Now Mon Tate was the outfit's cook, en he was drivin' the chuck-wagon. He says that folks kept a-watchin' every move he made. Most of 'em was ragged en bare-footed, with snuff-sticks hangin' out o' their mouths, en plumb eaten up with chills en fever, en takin' quinine en black draught as regular as their meals.

"Finally, Ike said, they got quite a bunch of little swamp cattle together en started west, buyin' a few from time to time as they went along.

"One evening, Ike said he was bringin' a little bunch o' cattle he had bought up to the wagon to throw into the herd, when he saw some one dodge behind a tree. Not knowin' what to think of it, he told Mon Tate to keep a close watch on the wagon en camp, as the feller he had seen might want to steal or something. Then the next day he again saw some one dodge behind a tree, en leavin' the herd jumped his horse over to where he had seen the man disappear, but in the thick underbrush he couldn't find no sign of him.

"Well, after buyin' all the cattle they could get, they started fer the river, en arrivin' at its banks, bedded down the herd en camped fer the night. Ike said as he went on guard he saw a man a-runnin' through the big trees along the river banks, but although he takes after him the man disappeared in the dark. Ridin' back to the wagon he tells the boys about it en edvised 'em when they're on guard, to be sure en pack their six-shooters, as yer never could tell what mischief these swamp hounds might be up to. Howsumever nothin' happened, en the next mornin' they swam the herd across the river en got into No Man's Land, as it was then called.

"Well, fer that matter, durin' the whole next week nothin' happened, but one mornin' jest as the herd was goin' off the bed-ground, Ike saw a man a-foot come out of a sand arroya lookin' like the same feller who had been dodgin' round the camp fer a couple o' weeks past.

"Ike jerks down his rope takes after him, en after quite a run catches him. Ike said he was the skinniest feller he had ever seen. With his prisoner walkin' ahead, he marches over to camp where the other punchers had jest arrived with the herd.

" 'What have you to got to say fer yourself?' says Ike to the prisoner.

" 'Nothin', Mister, I ain't er-meanin' no harm.'

" 'Ain't you the same feller has been dodgin' round our camp since we left the mountains in Arkansas?'

" 'I be,' says the swamp-angel.

" 'What's the idea o' follering us all this time? Are yer tryin' to get away with somethin'?' said Ike.

" 'No, I bein't,' says the feller.

" 'Look here,' says Ike gettin' real rough in his manner, 'if you don't tell us what you mean by hangin' around our outfit, we're aimin' ter shoot you full o' holes, en likewise murder en kill you. Get that?'

" 'Please, Mister, I ain't a-meanin' no harm.'

" 'Well, what are yer follerin' us for'? yells all the punchers together.

" 'Please, sirs, I never did see a wagon with two sets er wheels before, en I was jest follerin' along ter see when those big ones behind was a-goin' ter catch up with the little ones in front.'

" 'And that,' said Ike Clubb, pointin' to the fat man beside him, 'is how our dodgin' friend Brewster came to Oklahoma.' "

LINCOLN'S WAGER

"Huh, huh, huh! Oh Lord!"

"What's the matter, Tobe? What's the matter?"

"Well, yer ought ter have been there."

"Maybe so; what's the joke?"

"Well, yer know that station called Florida?"

"Yer."

"Well, yer know Cook's Peak? En yer know that little creek about half way?"

"Yer."

"Well, right there it happened."

"What happened?"

"Yer ought-a seen him."

"Who?"

"That fool Englishman."

"Well, what Englishman, en what did he do? Come through, now."

"Well, I was a-ridin' the creek this morning, pullin' stock out o' boggy places, en about noon I come to the old wagon crossin'. Yer know the road that runs to the west o' the peak en ambles west to the Membres River? Well, that the e-dentical place. Well, I sees a feller sittin' down on the bank en as I rides up he turns round en faces me.

" 'How!' says I to be sociable.

" 'How what?' says he.

" 'How d' yer do?' says I in my best Dallas style.

" 'Oh, awfully well, don't yer know,' says he, 'though a trifle fatigued.'

" 'I don't get yer,' says I.

" 'A bit overdone,' says he.

" 'Try it some other way', says I.

" 'I mean, I'm quite tired', says he.

" 'Why didn't yer say so'? says I, feelin' quite sorry fer him.

"From what little English he spoke I made out he had walked from Florida Station that morning, en had made the twenty miles in about five hours across all the hot sand, fetlock-deep, en not a drop of water on the road. Sure must have been driftin'.

"Well, settin' there we gets real sociable. I tells him my name's Tobe Gallus, en he kind o' lets it leak out that he's called Lord Lincoln, en he'd come up on the train that left Deming that mornin'.

"After I has smoked up his cigarettes he tells me he has made a wager.

" 'I don't get you, Mr. Lord. Say that again.'

" 'Wager,' says he.

" 'How do you make one of them?' says I.

" 'Oh, I believe you chaps call it a bet', says he.

" 'Yer bet we does', says I.

"Say, Ike, did yer ever meet up with one o' them Lords? They're the hardest people yer ever saw to save. Well, we sat there on the bank fer an hour or so, him tellin' me what jack-pots he had got into since comin' to America. Seems he'd been workin' over on a ranch on the big mesa, to 'get experience' as he told me, en through writing a letter home, had been accused by his folks of lyin'.

" 'Cut the deck a little deeper, en explain yourself', says I.

" 'Well', says he, 'back in England, yer know, all the cows are milked by milk-maids, en no one has over ten or a dozen cows, en of course keep them only for milkin, purposes, don't yer know?'

"I told him he had already asked me twice if I didn't know, en I'd have to say that I didn't, but to go right along.

" 'Well, on my uncle's ranch, after I went there to work, they told me that the ranch contained ten thousand cows, en I wrote home informing my people of the fact, expressly stating that my uncle had so informed me, when what was my surprise, upon receiving a reply to my letter, to find my own very dear brother, Lord Cecil, informed me that he thought I had acquired the American habit of yarnin', in fact did not believe anything of the sort, fer as he argued, where in the world could we get the milk-maids to milk this prodigious number of cows, don't yer know?'

"Well, all the time he'd been handin' me out this armful o' talk (en me a-wonderin' if the folks back in England were all so poor that they couldn't own over ten or twelve cows), the lord has been takin' his clothes off, but me bein' so interested in his talk I hadn't a-noticed what he was a-doin', till I sees him standin' there naked en rollin' his clothes up in a little bundle.

" 'I say, old top', says he to me, 'you have a horse, en would you mind, after I swim across, bringin' my clothes ter me?'

"Right then I sure thought he had gone loco for good. 'Swim', says I, 'can't yer see the creek is only three feet wide, en there ain't over two or three inches o' water in it?'

" 'Never mind, old chap', says he. 'You can't spoof me.' (That last word got me) 'I shall win my wager, though distances in this country are indeed deceitful. I shall make your Cook's Peak before night, fer as yer may not quite understand, my wager with these chaps on the train was that I could walk from that bally station back there to your Cook's Peak before nightfall, en even though the width o' this river may be as deceitful as the distance to the Peak I shall swim it, though I may be an hour in the water.'

"En in he jumps."

SHORTY'S BULL

"Shorty, it's around to you. Who have you been murderin' gettin' engaged to or divorced from since you was here last spring?"

"I ain't murdered anyone, or got engaged to anyone you could tell of, en the only divorcin' I've been lined up with was last fall in Kansas City, when a girl with a sacred bull divorced me from my whole year's roll. I didn't aim ever a say a word about it," says Shorty Mann, "but Lon Roberts over there was with me most o' the time, en as I can see he's jest a-tremblin' to make it worse than it was, I might as well come through.

"I got into Kansas City on Christmas Eve with a trainload o' Tumble-H cattle, most all aged steers en fat, en belongin' to old man Provost. I goes over to the Arcade Hotel en gets me a couple of warmers, en goes in to supper. At the same table sets a brown hided feller en a dark-skinned girl. We feeds en talks awhile, then all gets up at about the same time en goes out to the desk. I buys the gent a cigar en we lights up, the girl standin' beside us. I had about eight hundred dollars in my inside pocket, en I pulls it out, en shuckin' off a twenty, hands the balance to the clerk to put in the safe, which he done. Then we all go over en sits down.

"The old man en the girl was as pleasant as pie. Presently the hombre rubs his hand over his head, en says he to the girl; 'Daughter, I feel one o' my blindin' headaches comin' on, en think I'll trot off ter bed.'

" 'All right, Daddy', says the girl. 'But I want to see all the folks go by so I won't go to bed yet.''

"As this was Christmas Eve, there was great doin's outside, torch-light parades en folks dressed up in fancy dresses. Presently a big fat clown ran by the door, en jumpin' up the girl hollers, 'Let's go en see the fun': so I grabs my hat en we lights out. Say, that girl was plumb full of pep, en hand in hand we jest flew ter keep up with the mob. Presently when we'd seen about all we wanted en was a-passin' a movie, I said, 'Lets go in en see the show,' en in we went.

"Well, from watchin' my girl so close I disre- member all about the show but the girl next to me was jest grand. It was a long reel, en after it was over I says, 'Let's go in somewhere en get some sup- per.' She was game, en we goes into one of them cafés that had music. You swaller a oyster, grabs your girl, en dance once around the place, eats anoth- er oyster en dance again. Finally, when we gets to eatin' real earnest, I asks here what her name might be, en she tells me Diana King en they had jest come from Brownville, Texas, but before that from India. From what she told me I learned they was show peo- ple and had been exhibitin' a sacred bull which made 'em lots o' money; but as they had received a letter from her aunt in Chicago that her father's brother was not expected to live, they was a-goin' ter leave as soon as they could make arrangements fer the care o' their sacred bull.

"Well, we talked a lot, en presently the clock

in the big hall struck twelve, en she said, 'My but it's late! What will Daddy say? I'll have to go.' En as I said good night to her in the hotel lobby, she promised to take me over next mornin' en show me the bull. After she'd gone to bed I saunters up to the hotel register en there as plain as could be written, 'Captain Lycurgus King and Miss Diana King of Brownsville, Texas.'

"Well, boys, my dreams that night was all a mixture o' that girl surrounded by a bunch o' bulls, en when I waked up the next mornin' I was jest worn out from what I'd been through defendin' her from those vicious brutes.

"Early next mornin' I gets on my good suit, buys me a shave, en presently Diana comes down alone, sayin' her daddy was still sufferin' with a headache en had not slept a wink. The two of us then goes in and has breakfast, she all the time talkin' about Rajah, as she called the sacred bull. After breakfast we drifts over to the stock-yards where she had the Sacred One in a box-stall. Presently we finds him. Say, he sure was a beauty, though as Diana tells me goin' over, so far he had only had one master, her father, to whom he was greatly attached.

"Passin' by a market, Diana bought some carrots en spinach, en when we got to the stall the Holy One eat them out of her hand—who wouldn't? The door of the stall was cut in two, en as we opened it a feller in overalls carryin' a pitchfork come up en wants to know if we owns him. Diana tells him she does, en he says there was a feller lookin' at him a little earlier, en to tell the owner he would pay a thousand dollars fer him. 'Who was it?' asked Diana. 'Well, here is the card he gave me,' en takin' it, Di reads, 'Waltzingham Bates.'

" 'W-a-l-t-z-i-n-g-h-a-m B-a-t-e-s. The miserable skin-flint! He swindled my dear daddy out of three thousand dollars, and now he has the cheek to try en get Rajah away from us. He shall never have him!'

"We was a-standin' there en admirin' the Only One, me wonderin' why they put that hump on his back, when a busy little feller comes up en asks if we own the bull. Di says she does. Then he tells her she must have him out of that stall by noon as there's a string o' race-horses a-comin' en the bull has to go.

" 'Ain't there any more stalls?' asked Diana.

" 'No, madam, everything is full up.'

" 'Oh, what shall I do?' says Di.

" 'Maybe we should get a hustle on us en look for another place,' says I. At last, a block from the stock-yards, we found a toughlookin' guy who had a box stall, en though he said he would rent it he would not be responsible fer the welfare of any bull. Well, the stockyards people sent the Holy One over, en we saw him safely put away with his lip hangin' over a bale o' hay.

"As it was gettin' close to twelve o'clock we ambles back to the hotel, but all the way over Di hardly let a yap out of her. 'What's the matter?' I says. 'Oh,' she says, 'I dread goin' to Chicago en leavin'

Rajah with that desperate-lookin' man.' 'Why don't you sell him then?' I says. 'Brother Waltzingham offered you a thousand fer him.' 'Oh, he shall never have him. I would rather, if I can't make suitable arrangements fer his care, sell him fer half price. Waltzingham shall never have him.

'He is the only Hindustani bull in the world who can stand on his hind legs, walk around, en then kneel down en pray. Daddy has in his room the prayer-rug Rajar kneels on, en the Hindustani costume he wears while puttin' the bull through the act.'

"Well, as we go into the hotel, we see Captain Lycurgus comin' down the stairs, en though he says he can't eat anything we all go into the dinin'-room together. Di tells her daddy all her troubles en also about Waltzingham. When Lycurgus heard the name he almost had a fit. He, like Di, declares Waltz' shall never have him, en goes into details en tells me how the said Waltz' Bates had swindled him out o' the three thousand dollars. Finally after a lot of talk Di says that although they hate to part with Rajah, if they could only be assured he would receive a good home, they would sell him at a sacrifice. Well, it all ended up by me buyin' him fer six-fifty, they agreein' ter throw in the prayer-rug en Hindustani clothes.

"After dinner I pays the money, gets the clothes, en I'm a real show-man. They then give me a bill o' sale en an order on the keeper who has him in charge. The old man en I take a few to cinch the deal, en I go up to his room to try on my new outfit. Say, it was sure gaudy, pair o' turned up slippers, worked in gold beads, wide white pants felt like silk, black lace short jacket with white ruffled shirt, en a round red cap with a black tassel hangin' to it. The prayer-rug was white en blue, en in the center had the word 'Mizpah' on it in red letters.

"After I got rigged out, Di comes a-runnin' in en hands the Captain a telegram which he reads, en puttin' his handkerchief to his nose hands the message to me. It says. 'Brother Alfred very low come at once, signed Anna'. They went at once.

"I was so tickled with my new clothes that I went down stairs with 'em on, en who should I run into but this big stiff Lon Roberts, but he never knew me till I tells him who I am, en we had several. 'What in hell are you doin' in those fancy clothes; goin' to a ball?' 'No, you poor cow-puncher I'm in the show business, got me a sacred bull with a hump on his back big as a feather bed. Ever see one?' 'Nope', says he, 'where is he? Let's have one,' Lon says. We did.

"Well, after several more we decides to go over en have a look at Rajah. The tough-lookin' gypsy in charge was a-standin' outside the stall leanin' against a post when we arrived. Waltzing up I gives him the order fer the bull which after lookin' over he grunts *bueno*. Lon, as I afterwards remember, was born down in Brownsville, but at the time I had forgotten all about it. Well, I throws open the door o' the box-stall en shows Lon my six hundred en fifty beauty. 'Fine, ain't he?' I asks. 'Fine, sure,' says Lon, 'I've seen herds of 'em back home. Say, he's a hump-backed Bramah, or as we call 'em in Texas, a Brimer. He'll weigh about a thousand pounds en bring yer three cents a pound at the butcher's. Well, Lon here sure said a truth, fer after subtractin' the feed bill fer a week he fetched jest nineteen dollars, en the feller I sold him to told me he had him cut out of a car-load of others which had arrived from southern Texas a week before, as he was too thin to butcher.''

"Well, Shorty," commented the foreman, "that was some bull any way yer take it."

"Say," said Shorty, "yer ain't a-thinkin' I lost on the deal are yer?"

"Well, yer ain't said much ter make me calculate your winnin's in the millions, Shorty."

"Sure. But you ain't been over to my shack yet either. Jest drop around some time en I'll have yer meet Di en the kid."

"Di en ———?"

"Yep. Named him Rajah, en now I'm busy watchin' him grow ter see if he's goin' ter have a hump on his back or no."

And with that, Shorty Mann left the group around the chuck-wagon and began deliberately to search for his bedding.

LOCO

"Squatty en I had been workin' all season with the Y-O wagon, gatherin' en shippin' what a two-years' drought had left o' the Doc Nichol's stock. We sold out the remnant en brand to a neighborin' ranchman, who had bought the ranch en improvements; en from him we in turn bought two carloads o' old, fat, locoed horses, or rather they were given to us, en as it was understood that we were to ship 'em out o' the state, we didn't have to vent, or counter-brand 'em; as we were headed fer an eastern market the fact of our not havin' to burn 'em any more would help toward their sale.

"Say, that bunch had all been locoed two years before, en had run on the home alfalfa place fer eight months en were hog fat, but there wasn't a one of 'em that would dare step over a rope. Loco's the Spanish word for crazy, en the definition's right.

"We pulled out o' the stock-yards at Deming at one o'clock o' the mornin' o' June the tenth (I remember because it was the day I was supposed to been born) after fightin' since six the night before to get the locos into the car. Squatty was loaded, en the fact that I had been celebratin' my birthday didn't help any in gettin' that crazy bunch aboard.

"Well, we billed 'em to Hopgate, Tennessee, where Squatty and a cousin o' his had an uncle, en though he had never seen him he knew we sure would be welcome. Some drummer Squatty had met twenty years before had told him that horses back there was worth a fortune, so off we goes. Squatty confides in

me that though out here niggers was a kind of a curiosity, back there they raised 'em regular. In fact
most everyone was black, though he didn't mention
his cousin's uncle.

"Next thing of any importance was when we un-
carred at Dallas, Texas, when a feller walks up to us
(as we was a-sittin' on the stock-yard fence watchin'
them locos eat up our dollars in hay at a dollar a
package), en says he:

" 'You alls own this stock?'

"Squatty says, 'Sure.' Then the freckled-faced
gents wants to know what Squatty's name was, en
when Squatty tells him he wants to see a bill o' sale
fer the horses. Course as they was given to us, as
we up en explains, we didn't have any bill o' sale.
Then the gent proceeds to introduce himself as High
Jenkins, Stock Inspector, and we was both under
arrest.

"Well, to get back to now, we give him the man's
name what we got the stock from, en after eighteen
dollars' worth o' telegraphin' they telegraphed us a
bill o' sale all made out regular before a notary public en signed, en they let us go, damn him—I mean
the Inspector.

"Well, he bumped along into New Orleans en
got there about midnight, told 'em to feed our stock,
en started out to rustle a hotel en found one called
the Comet, en a nigger boy showed us up to the second
floor, opened the door, lit the gas en asked, 'Is there
anything you wants, Boss?' Squatty tells the boy to

bring a bottle o' whiskey en a bucket of ice water, en to come a-runnin'.

"In about two minutes up comes the coon with the implements, en as he starts out points to the gas jet, en says he, 'Boss, don't blow it out; turn it out,' en about then Squatty's boot catches the shine on his left hip pocket, en out he goes a-flyin' but still hollerin', 'Don't blow it out, Boss.'

"After carrin' up the horses and a two day's run, we arrives at Hopgate in the middle o' the night as usual, en as they had no stock-yards we had to leave 'em in the cars till mornin'. After a hot night en not much of a breakfast we sauntered down to see about our horses.

"Everybody in western Tennessee was there to see the broncs, as they call back there any horse that carries a brand.

" 'Boss, is dey for sale?'

" 'How much fer de spotted one?'

" 'Does yer have to have der cash to buy one?'

" 'Say Mister, can Ise help yous take dem off de cars; I had a cousin Dave dat worked on a ranch in Texas when he was a boy en I knows all about dese mustangs.'

"The next mornin' as we were workin' around the pens, an old rail-bird happened along en begun tellin' me his family history. Seems he was the seventh son of a seventh daughter en had always been unlucky, had had lots o' trouble the last four years. He'd lost four good horses. Every one of 'em had fallen into the same open well in his pasture. Now what did I know about that? He was thinkin' o' movin' out o' the state en wanted to know about the climate o' New Mexico. Did I think it would help his old woman, who had been ailin' fer more than eight years? Yep, she was in-valid, in fact. (I believed it would).

"He next noticed the angora goat-hair saddle-pockets on my saddle en asked me what they might be made of. I told him quite truthful—made from the hide of an angora goat, the kind we had in New Mexico. He next got hold of a raw-hide rope I had hung on my saddle en wanted to know how long it was en what it might be made of. I told him it was made from a calf's hide en was about thirty-five feet long. 'Look-a here, young feller,' he said, 'you may make some folks believe that goats in New Mexico have hair six inches long, but by dad, you needn't think I'm damn fool enough to believe that calves out there grow to be thirty five feet long.'

"Well, after unloadin' en hazin' 'em over to a pen back o' the livery stable where we thought we had better feed 'em fer a day or two before startin' a sale, I heard Squatty askin' an old man if he knew where Caleb Robinson lived, which was the name o' the uncle o' the cousin he had so often spoken about but never seen. 'Yep, I know him well,' replied the old party; 'he all lives about two sites en a horn's blow the other side o' yon mountain.'

" 'Yer don't say so,' says Squatty, winkin' at me, 'By hell!'

"Well, after advertisin' in the local paper three days, which notice none o' the darkies could read, we started a sale. We told everyone to bring a strong rope who intended buyin' a bronc, en several friends to help him lead it away. No horse could be taken out o' the corral till all were sold. Then we would rope each horse and put the owner's rope on him. These were the terms o' the sale.

"Well, it took the combined efforts of about two hundred darkies of all sizes and ages till sundown to get 'em out o' the corral, en most of 'em till midnight to get 'em home, en some didn't get 'em home at all."

JIM RED'S CHRISTMAS RIDE

"After carefully thinkin' it over en sizin' it up with the other towns, Nogal was decided on as the place where Jim Red would spend his Christmas, as he heard all the other cow-punchers would be there."

Now Jed Foster has been sitting around the same chuck-wagon with me a good many years, and I never did see yet but what he was good and willing to spill a yarn. No kicking or fussing, either, like some of these punchers. It was just:

"What's yours, Jed?"

"Same's yours."

"Say! I mean, what yer goin' to do fer us?"

And after his little joke he would start, as I've shown at the beginning here.

"After carefully thinkin' it over en sizin' it up with the other towns, Nogal was decided on as the place where Jim Red would spend his Christmas, as he heard all the other cow-punchers would be there."

Jed would be off, then, with nothing to stop him.

"After gettin' a week's lay-off en drawin' a hundred dollars from the Circle-W Boss, Jim put on his best suit o' clothes, en saddlin' up old Rooster, quickly covered the twelve miles between the ranch en town. Tyin' up his horse in the corral, he saunters down towards the saloon where someone inside, spyin' him, hollers, 'Last man in town's treat!' En it didn't take Jim very long ter get his money in circulation.

"Well, now the game o' poker needs steady practice to keep your hand in, as Jim found out to his cost, en as his trips to town had been few (never comin' except between round-ups), it didn't take him long to part company with half his roll and gather up a talkin' load.

"So, decidin' that he would get a better run at the bar for his money he got up from the table en invited all hands to drink.

"Now five days' straight dancin' en drinkin' without any sleep when the licker's bad, don't put yer in the best o' humor with the world, or with yourself, either; so after sayin' *Adios* to everybody, not forgettin' the new biscuit-shooter at the hotel, Jim, armed with a quart, starts fer the ranch. At least that was what he thought. But the night bein' dark, en old Rooster's range in another direction, they pulls up about nine o'clock at an old board shack at the Milagra Springs, jest as a comfortable snow storm sets in.

"Jim managed to unsaddle and tie up the horse, en draggin' his saddle and blankets into the shack, got ready fer his first sleep in five nights.

"He found he didn't have no matches, though they would have been useless without wood, candle, or lamp, so he settles himself down on his saddle blankets tryin' to be as contented en comfortable as possible.

"He'd just laid down when what looked like two

small lamps shone in the far corner, which, after studyin' 'em awhile, turned into a pair of eyes.

"Now Jim feared nothin' in the world but skunks, but was, like all cow-punchers, afraid o' bein' mad bit.

"Well, first he threw a small stone he found at the animal, or whatever it might be, then his hat, his quirt, en his bridle, finally gettin' up when it wouldn't move en shootin' all the catridges out o' his six-shooter at it. But still it wouldn't go. Gettin' mad Jim took after it, pistol in hand, but the faster Jim ran, the faster the animal, en always managed ter keep just a little ahead of him.

"At last, tired out en not too steady on his legs, Jim give up the chase en lay down on his blankets, sayin' half aloud that it was damn cold. 'Yes,' answered the animal, 'it is.' By this time, to Jim, it had turned itself into a giant cat.

"Jim, still gazin' unsteadily at the cat, studied fer some moments, then made a wild jump fer his saddle en blankets, sayin' that it was goin' to be a damn' sight colder where he was goin'; en draggin' saddle en blankets out into the cold, began saddlin' his horse.

"Scared is the word, en scared right was Jim, en puttin' spurs en quirt to old Rooster, he headed in a straight line for the home ranch. He keeps the old horse at a pretty hot pace fer seven or eight miles, then pullin' up says to him,' 'We've had a pretty stiff run.'

" 'Yes,' says the cat, who Jim saw was hangin' to his stirrup, 'we have.'

"Jim's only reply, as round-eyed he digs the rowls into Rooster en starts on the last ten-mile heat fer the ranch, was, 'Yes, we've had a hot run, but by heck we'd have a darn sight hotter one if I had another catridge fer my six-shooter.'

"Well, the boys say about sun-up they saw Jim ride up to the ranch-house, en in the next week they was busy pickin' up en buryin' all the cats Jim had shot around the place."

SALAU

"You boys remember when they started to open up the coal fields over in the Salau country? Well, early one spring a bunch of us pulled out from Black River huntin' a job with the Blocks, but as spring work hadn't commenced en they charged us thirty-five cents a meal, we kept a-goin' till we got to Salau. As wages was good en not much of anything else doin', we all took a job till spring work opened up. Salau took a boom, whiskey went up, en the proof of it went down. As the company opened up more mines they found they was in need of a boarding-house, en the first hotel was opened in Salau by Waverly Thompson.

"Waverly was an old cow-puncher who had married a widow with two grown sons en a small bunch o' cattle; she was a natural born hustler en jest what Waverly needed, as her hustling kind o' offset his love-to-sit-on-the-sunny-side-of-the-house-en-roll - a- cigarette habits. The old woman did the work en the old man handled the cash—at least a part of it. Except fer a few family rows en once in a while a spree by the old man, they got along fine. They had lots o' boarders, Swedes, Portuguese, Bohemians, en English, en when they was talkin' at meal-time it sounded like a log chain was bein' dragged over a cobble-stone street.

"Well, the boarding house in a straight line was not over half a mile from the store, but as all the ground between had been dug full of holes, two by six feet en from four to sixty feet deep accordin' to the dip o' the coal vein, yer had to go around 'em to get from the boarding house to the store, en it was quite a trip.

"The cow men had lost a lot o' cattle in these holes en had made the superintendent o' the mine put a log over the tops ter keep the cattle from fallin' in.

"Well, on Thanksgiving morning after his early cup o' coffee Waverley saddled old Paint and told Ma, as he called his wife, that he was a-goin' down to the store fer the mail which had come in the night before.

" 'Come home early,' she hollered as the old man rode off.

"Now when you know you'll get a Tom-en-Jerry at the expense of the store keeper, it don't take long with a good horse to cover a mile, so in about four jiffs Waverley had fallen off Paint en left him standing in front of old Sieb's store.

" 'Mornin' all.'

" 'Jest in time, Waverley.   One o' my own brews.'

"Well, where there's a hot one on every game, time passes quick, en a little after sun-down Waverley thought it was time to take that letter he'd got in the mail up to the shack.

"Getting the outer door in line, he made it without any trouble, but outside was no horse.   Paint, after waitin' a couple of houre en not knowin' it was

Thanksgiving, had started fer home, so now it was a question of stay all night or walk. Thinking that the old woman would be up a-waitin' fer him, he decided it was best to walk, en after figurin' the length o' the wagon-road as against the dangers o' the short cut, he takes the latter.

"Cold it was, but with all the Tom-en-Jerrys in side of him en his coat collar turned up, he started; fer a cow-puncher's got to have more troubles than an ordinary man if he's not lighthearted. So, whistlin', he started across lots fer the shack.

"Though the night was dark, across the flat he could see the lantern a-hangin' outside the door on a post, but he thought it was queer it swung so when not a breath of air was a-stirrin', but at last he makes up his mind that it was still.

"Says he to himself: 'It's that damn horses's fault, Paint!'

"It got awful cold, but he was makin' it, even if he hadn't covered over a hundred yards since leavin' the store half an hour ago.

" 'Never mind, I see lights. Tell yer, it hits a feller after comin' out of a hot room'.

"He rocks along, always a-keepin' his eyes on the lantern ahead, till all at once he feels himself fallin.' Now he savvied he'd stepped into a prospect hole, so he made a wild grab, en by good luck caught hold of a top post, one of those thrown across these holes ter save cattle. In what part o' the flat the hole was he couldn't figure out but at last he makes up his mind it was one of the last holes dug, en if so it must be at least sixty feet deep.

"Well, he tried ter get one leg over the pole, but with his heavy overcoat en load couldn't make it. Then he called, 'Sieb!' but no reply, Sieb bein' in the store pourin' out jest one more.

"He sticks there till his arms pains en begins ter swell, then he does something that no Waverley had never done before—began to pray!

'Oh Lord, please get me out of this Jack-pot en I won't beat the old woman any more. Jest this once! I know I been wicked, but oh Lord, remember I never had no raisin', I was only jest jerked up by the hair of the head. Oh Lord, fergive me fer bein' too liberal with my brandin' iron, sometimes gettin' it on the wrong calf, because oh Lord, you've been a man yerself en know how these things are.' Then he sang awhile from 'Jordan's Icy Mountains', or whatever it is.

"Well, after another short prayer en askin' the old woman to forgive him, knowin' that his hands wouldn't hold him no longer, en expecting to be smashed to pieces, he turns loose en falls ter what he thinks is certain death.

"The next morning,' as the boys was goin' ter work they heard someone holler, en walkin' up to one of the holes they sees Waverley in the bottom of on? seven feet deep. He had just fallen one foot."

BOWDER JIM'S HOUND

Caleb Small, who worked for the L F D outfit over on the plains, came to the wagon one night with a bunch of our horses which they had found across the river during the horse work, and which the foreman had sent back to us. As I knew Caleb was from Texas I asked him how long since he had eaten any 'possum, leading him on till he told us the following story:

"Yer know, the best coon en 'possum hunting country in Texas is in the big Trinity River bottoms which is covered with heavy timber en has the best kind of hunting for anyone who's got a hound dog. Lots of squirrel, 'possum, en coons, en once in a while a deer, though the deer have been mostly killed off.

"It had been talked about (the part of the bottom where I lived, which was called Jordan on account o' the number o' darkies livin' there) that on the next Saturday night Major Wren (who was the most richest white planter in that neighborhood) would have some gemmen from Dallas stoppin' with him who had never seen a coon hunt, en more specially one at night by torch light. Word was sent that everyone was invited to meet at a certain point en bring their guns en torches en hounds fer a hunt: afterwards all was invited to a dance in the Major's coach-house.

"Well, at the place they'd agreed on, over a hundred o' the crack coon hunters o' the country met with their hounds en guns each tryin' to kill

more game than the other feller, en such a yelpin'
and a collection o' hounds I never before seed. The
night en wind bein' jest right, forty coons en 'pos-
sums was killed, after which they all headed fer the
Major's, comin' in little bunches from different parts
of the woods with terrible tales accordin' as they'd
had good or bad luck.

"The Major en his friends, after they'd got the
dance goin', called a little bunch o' the oldest hunters into his room, en after givin' a few glasses o'
punch to each, asked them to tell his friends some of
their hunting stories. Yer know in this kind of hunting of coon en 'possum at night almost everything
depends on your dog, so the main part of this story
runs on the intelligence of him. They sure told some
stories till there was but two of them left, Rush Pi
en old Bowder Jim, who, as the Major afterwards
told us, were old rivals, each havin' his little bunch of
friends who claimed he was the best hunter in the
bottoms.

"Well, Rush Pi, after a number of coughs, tells
how his hound Painter had once treed a coon, 'en ac-
tually sat under dat tree, whined, barked, en watched
dat coon till he plumb starved to death, en when dey
found dem de coon had done turned gray wid de old
age.'

"Well, when he finished that story the other
darkies looked at one another, wonderin' if old
Bowder Jim could beat that.

" 'Major,' begins Bowder, 'yer know dat old

hound what got der blue patch on der side o' der haid? Well sar, der daddy o' dat dog was der smartest dog dat ever I seen. 'Bout six years ago Mr. Courtney come down here en get me ter go huntin' wid him, en I brings along der old hound what was der daddy of old Blue, en we gets in der wagon wid more guns, Major, den I could shoot in ma whole life. Down past der cottonwood crossin' we goes, den Mr. Courtney en me gets out en I projects around for a fresh trail. Directly we strikes it, en old Fanny (dat's one of Mr. Courtney's) says: "O-ough", den dey all hollers together, "Ough," en directly I sees a deer jump. Up der hill he go en into der brush and out o' sight. 'Bout den Mr. Courtney he sees de deer en holler, "Bowder! Bowder! get yer hound en put on der trail too! Him's a big buck—must be nine or ten years old!" So I puts der hounds on der trail, der dady of old Blue in der lead, en me en Mr. Courtney gets der guns en comes along behind.

" 'Somehow, Major, der daddy of old Blue started a-runnin der wrong way on dat trail en go der way der deer come from. Yes sar, en der daddy of old Blue trails dat deer, and trails dat deer, en just kep' on a-trailin' dat deer, till we hears, four years after dat, he done trailed him back to der very spot where he was bawn. Dat's what he done, Major.' "

DUBLIN AND THE KID

"Well, Jingle Bob", asked Latham, "what was that yarn you was tellin' about the Irishman who worked over at the old Governor's ranch when you were there?"

"Which one?" asked Jingle Bob.

"That tale you told about the feller who lost the kid."

"Well,", replied Jingle Bob, "that wasn't anything but jest so. I'll tell yer. The pipe-smokin', book-readin' fool. If yer don't believe me jest ask Mac. Though he wasn't runnin' the ranch then, he knows all about it. Yer see, there was an imported feller named Jimmy Albright who was general manager at that time, en he had a little kid, about a yearling. Him and his Missus jest naturally think this kid is the only one that had ever been portioned out to New Mexico. They'd fixed it all up with a foreign name, had it baptized, en it was a sure-enough handsome kid, en all the punchers thought it was all right.

"You know the old Governor's ranch?"

"Nope."

"Well, it controlled all the range north en south from Red Lake to the sink-holes in the White Sands, almost a hundred miles, en from the White Mountains and Sacramentos on the east to the Oscuros, en San Andres on the West.

"The old headquarters ranch at Carrizozo was jest a big square old adobe house, built to stand the

Indians off, en it was sure strong enough to do it. All around the ranch-house the ground was covered with taboso or salt grass humps, en it was pretty rough sleddin' till you got away en struck the Carrizozo flats.

"Well, it seemed that this feller Dublin I'm tellin' yer about, heard there was a foreigner runnin' the ranch, en one evening about sundown he steps off a freighter's wagon that was passin' the ranch, comin' in from San Antonio on the railroad ninety miles to the west. All he brought with him was what he called a rain-coat—though it wouldn't turn any rain—en his pipe.

"After he gets down from the wagon he moseys up en asked me (I was shoein' a horse) where the Boss lived, en I points him the big house. Fer the next few days we sees him en Jimmy (that's the Boss's name) walkin' around, talkin' en a-smokin' regular. One mornin' the Boss tells me to saddle up old Robin, en that Dublin, which was this new feller's name, will ride out with me to help get up the saddle horses. So I does so, en off we ambled.

"Well, I see right then this feller don't know anything about a horse. When we gets to the pasture I tells him to drive the west fence en I'll drive the east one, en we'll throw our bunches of horses together at the gate as we come out. Well, we gets to the end o' the pasture en starts back all right. The horse pasture bein' long en narrow, I could see Dublin all the time. When he starts back he had maybe forty head in his bunch, en they all run back to the

far end o' the pasture. Presently he turned old Robin around en starts after 'em on the prettiest little
walk yer ever see. When I saw what was happenin'
I jumped my horse off, heads 'em, en throws 'em into my bunch. After a while he catches up with me,
en I says: 'What did yer let 'em get by yer for?'
'Oh,' he replied, 'my pipe went out, you know, en I
had to get a light, you know.' 'Fine,' says I, 'that's
what the Boss pays yer fer', en he gives me the queer-
est look yer ever saw.

"Well, it wasn't long till the Boss found out this
hombre would never make a hand on a horse, so he
puts him to helpin' around the ranch. The first day
old Patten, the cook, sends him to the well fer water.
The well was about ten feet deep en had a rope with
a bucket on each end, the rope runnin' over a pully.
Presently Dublin comes back en asks Patten ter go
over to the well with him en show him how to get the
water out, as he didn't understand the method, as he
called it. They put him ter choppin' wood fer the
cook's stove, en after about an hour's work he almost
chopped his foot off, en was laid up in bed a month,
en then hobbled around on crutches or with a cane
all summer. But that jest seemed ter suit him, as he
could read and smoke his pipe all he wanted to.

"Well, one fine day Missus Jimmy (that was the
Boss's wife's name) started off to give the kid a
ride in the baby-buggy, when Dublin ups en offers
to do the job himself. 'All right,' says the Missus,
'but you must take good care of him.' 'Sure,' says
Dublin. I was in the saddlin' room fixin' up a sad-

dle when he passes by, pullin' the baby-buggy behind him, a big pipe in his face en a-readin' a book as he goes.

"I had to make several trips durin' the afternoon, back en forth from the saddlin' room to the commissary fer leather en rivets en different things. Every time I'd pass out or in I'd kind o' look in the direction Dublin had gone. Last time I saw him he was about a mile from the ranch out on the flats headin' towards the Mala Pais, head down en a-readin' hard. He was too far off fer me to see the smoke comin' out of his pipe, but I'll bet my saddle against a pair of OK spurs that she was a-workin'.

"There was no one at the ranch that afternoon except the Missus, the cook, en myself, all the rest o' the boys havin' ridden over to Coyote Springs to brand up any calves that might have been missed on the general work. Along late in the evenin' the Missus comes down to the shed where I'm workin', en asks me if I'd seen anything o' Dublin en I tells her where I'd seen him last about two hours before en I says I guess he will be back presently. Well, about an hour later, back she comes a-lookin' worried en asks again if I'd seen anything more o' Dublin, en did I think he would be back soon? Presently I seen a dust arisin' to the south, en I knew it was the boys a-comin' in from the calf-brandin'. By the time the sun was gettin' real low, up they rides en ties their horses to the hitching-rail en sets down on the gallery, turnin' in to the Boss talleys o' the calves each had branded.

"Just then around the cornor o' the ranch-house comes Dublin still smokin' his pipe, readin' his book, en pullin' the baby-buggy behind him. Missus Jimmy, who had been settin' in the gallery, on seein' Dublin turnin' the corner o' the house, started fer the buggy, callin' out to Dublin, 'How did my little darling behave?'

" 'Fine,' says Dublin.

" 'Did he cry any?' asks the Missus.

" 'Not a peep out of him,' says Dublin. 'Best behaved kid I ever saw.'

"By this time Missus Jimmy had got to the buggy, en throwin' off the cover she had put over the kid, let a scream out o' her like I once heard a Mescalero Indian squaw give. 'Dublin! Dublin!' says she, 'where is little Jimmy?'

"The bunch o' cow-punchers was too far away to hear any o' the talk between the Missus en Dublin, but by the time she had finished with her war whoop, nine punchers smellin' trouble were mounted en comin' hell-a-bent on their horses towards 'em. 'Whats the matter Missus? Did Dublin say something he hadn't oughter?' bellows Long Hyde, a-lookin' at Dublin. 'No, no!? squawls the Missus, 'he-he-low-low-los-lost little Jimmy Abercrombie.' 'Never mind Missus,' says Allen, 'we'll find him. Which way did you come in from' he asks Dublin.

"Soon they was all off on the hunt. The boys took the back trail o' the baby-buggy, which, bein' fresh, they followed on a lope. About two miles from the ranch they come on James Abercrombie Albright, Jr., fast asleep between two salt grass humps where Dublin had spilled him, bein' so busy readin' his novel en smokin' his pipe he had never missed him. In a short while nine cow-punchers rode back to the ranch, Shorty, bein' the one who had picked the baby up, havin' him in front of him in his saddle, delivers him up to the delighted Missus who comes a-runnin' out to meet them.

"After supper, the boys held a meetin' in the bunk house tryin' to figger out what they should do with, or, to, Dublin. Some recommened tyin' a tin can to him en turnin' him loose, en others was in favor o' ridin' him on a rail, but the majority was all fer Johnson givin' him a good talkin' to en advisin' him ter quit.

"So Johnson found Dublin, sittin' on the edge o' the gallery en lookin' kind o' glum, so he sat down with him.

" 'Dublin,' says Johnson, 'the boys ain't very well suited with your actions en decided you had better leave. Course I'm sorry fer yer. 'Taint exackly your fault ye're so green, its mostly the way yer been raised. 'Staid o' your people givin' yer an education, why didn't they teach yer something that would a been useful to yer, some good horse sense? Education without it won't never get yer nowhere, but if yer have good horse sense even without education, yer can travel a long way.'

"En as I told yer", finished Jingle Bob, "that yarn ain't anything but jest so."

KERN CARRICO

"One Mornin', bein' short o' cow-hands to make up my outfit," Dode Higgins began, "I walked into the Easy Concience Saloon, en who should I meet up with but old Kern Carrico.

" 'Hello, Kern,' I called, 'What yer doin'? Have a drink?'

" 'Sure will', replied Kern.

" 'You want a job?'

" 'I sure do,' he replied. 'I'm out o' work, busted, en jest got fired.'

" 'Where was yer workin' last?' I asked, fer I'd lost track of him fer some time but understood he had a steady job.

" 'Well, yer know Joe Nagle who runs the livery?' says Kern.

" 'Yep.'

" 'Well, I was a-hangin' round there fer my board, helpin' look after the horses, hitch up, en such like, Joe supplyin' the eats, en a few small ones occasionally, when one day that new Baptist preacher who bought the old Mullins House, drops in en orders out his horse en buggy.

" 'While I was a-hitchin' it up, he asked Joe if he happens ter know of a good man who wanted to work 'bout his lawn en fix it up, lay out some flower-beds en plant some geraniums en other flowers. Joe, winkin' at me, tells the preacher that I was a landscape gardner, en had jest finished layin' out the grounds 'round some Capitol Buildin's somewhere or other, en was now on my way to decorate the grounds o' the White House at Washington. As we were old friends I had stopped off a few days ter pay him a visit. Say, but Joe could always hand out a book when he had a few drinks ahead.

" 'Well, that preacher sure asked me a lot o' questions, especially 'bout myself, en how did I plant flowers, what was the best time o' year fer such variety, en a hundred other such fool things. I tells him if he hed spent as many years as I had a-learnin' the trade, he wouldn't tell all he knew without bein' paid fer it. Would he, huh?

" 'Well, at last he asked me what my religion was, en I was a Baptist, o' course. Well, that cinched the deal, all but the money part of it. Then he ups en tells me, that on the next day he was goin' back to St. Louis ter get married, en would be gone 'bout a month, en how long would it take me ter fix his place up? Well, I tells him, as I wasn't acquainted with the place, I would have ter go up en look it over with him, en after his showin' me what he wanted done, would then say if I wanted the job or not, as usually these small jobs didn't pay me fer layin' over.

" 'Well, I borrows an old tape line from Joe en up we goes. Well sir, I never was very good at figures, but in measurin' the size o' them beds he wanted laid out I couldn't remember if seven en eight made fourteen or seventeen, but o' course I never let on ter him I didn't know.

" 'Well, we pretty near wore that old tape out, en

finally I told him I'd take the job fer three hundred en twenty-five dollars. You ought ter heard him snort, said the price was outrageous, en lots of other things. Well, I tells him landscape-gardenin' is mighty hard work, en if he didn't like my price, maybe he could get some other man cheaper who would probably make a mess of it.

" 'Well, if it hadn't a-been I was Baptist, I don't believe he would a hired me, but he didn't feel as though he could turn down a brother o' the same faith. So we compromised on two hundred en seventy-five, one hundred down, the bank to pay me another hundred when work was completed, en the balance when he returned with his bride.

" 'Well, he gimme the hundred en left on the afternoon train fer the East. I exchanged five bones fer a gallon jug o' the Easy Consicence Saloon's best, Joe locked the livery stable door, en we went into session in the harness-room. We sure did some great plannin' as to how we would lay out that preacher's lawn.

" 'Over at Joe's house he had one o' them kaleidoscopes. We took it over to the barn, sent out fer another jug, en every time we'd turn the thing round we'd take a drink en try en draw a picture, the same as it looked through the end o' the kaleidy. Well sir, we put in a hard day a-copyin' them pictures, but it seemed the longer we worked on 'em the worse en more unreal they got. Presently Joe dropped the kaleidy on the floor, en it all smashed ter pieces, so that ended all the flower-bed drawin' fer that day.

" 'Then Nosey Potter the carpenter knocked on the door (Joe always said Nosey could smell licker a mile), en we let him in, give him a drink, en told him our troubles.

" 'Nosey said he had once studied drawin', but the more drinks he got into him the more his drawin's began to look like coffins, the makin' o' which was his principal way of earnin' a livin'.

" 'Well, another week went by en our plans weren't much further along than when we started, but the hundred the preacher had given me was fadin' fast. Well, we'd agreed as it was Saturday, that we'd better invest in some more Easy Conscience, en bright en early Monday mornin' start to work. By limitin' ourselves en skimpin' our drinks we managed ter make the jug hold out till Monday.

" 'Howsumever, 'bout breakfast time Monday Joe kind o' thought as we was a-passin' the Easy Conscience we'd better get a small bottle ter take along, but as they didn't have any pints we were jest forced to take a quart. After we'd climbed the hill where we left our lunch bucket, Joe suggested we'd better have one, so we did, then we got the tools out o' the barn en sat down to talk it over.

" 'I suggested that the first flower-bed should be in the shape of a diamond. Then I thought the next one should be a spade, but Joe insisted it oughter be a club. Club we made it, en the last flower-bed was the ace o' spades, Joe takin' a deck o' cards out o' his pocket as we worked, to see that we got the pattern right.

" 'It has always seemed a shame that when a man's workin' as we was, tryin' to make an honest livin', that neighbors won't leave 'em alone, instead of offerin' advice en hornin' in where they are not wanted. We had no sooner got those beautfiul beds cut out o' the sod than Mrs. Cox, the old busy-body, leaned her old reptile of a head over the hedge en called me a blank darn sacrilegious imp, to dessicate the lawn of one o' the Lord's chosen with the emblems of our vile trade. I didn't get her so I keeps on workin'.

" 'Next day we had five hundred red geraniums sent up, en we planted 'em real tight together in the beds, so they showed up sure red en pretty against the green lawn.

" 'While I was a-finishin' up the plantin', Joe was runnin' the mower en givin' the lawn a cuttin', en when we started home she sure did look grand. Everybody we met seemed ter be smilin', en Joe en I figured they was all well pleased with our job. Our credit was A-1, so on our way home we stepped into the Easy Conscience en had a couple, en on the strength o' the hundred which we were to receive in the mornin' we took a bottle home.

" 'Well, early as the bank opened in the mornin' Joe en I was there. The cashier who had been told to pay us when we were through, jest asked us to sign a receipt en passed us out the hundred dollars. Joe, who was pretty well posted on such matters, found that we could save ninety cents by buyin' two gallons at one time instead o' buyin' the two gallons separately. He encouraged our doin' so, en as I always did believe in savin' a penny wherever you could, I readily agrees, so we went home carryin' a jug apiece.

" 'Well, fer the followin' week everyone was tellin' us what a good job we'd done, en laughin' en slappin' us on the back till Joe commence ter want to take all the credit fer the beautiful job on himself.

" 'A couple weeks later the telephone rang in the office, which I answered, en who should it be but the Baptist preacher returned with his bride from his honeymoon. He asked me to who he was speakin', en when I told him he cut the traces loose.

"Looker here, Mr. Carrico," says he, "what have you been tryin' ter do? Make me, a minister o' the Gospel, the laughin'-stock o' my fellow citizens, en more especially of my flock? What do you mean by cuttin' the emblems o' the gambler upon my front lawn en makin' them more evident by fillin' them with red geraniums? You scoundrel, if I ever meet you I'll chastise you even though it may be in public."

" 'Well, I jest naturally couldn't keep up with him, so I dropped the phone en (I may add) the seventy-five dollars he owed me as well. Yes sir, I'm huntin' a job en the further away it is from here the better it'll suit me.' "

HEAVEN OR A STACK OF REDS

"The first time I ever saw George was over in Santa Fé. Seems to me it was jest after the Spanish invasion, 'way back before we got vaccinated with prohibition.

"I ain't much good on exact dates, but it sure was a long time ago. I was standin' on the sidewalk a-buzzin' one o' them little Spanish girls (sure pretty) when a puncher ups en asks me where he could fill a two-gallon keg that he was carryin' (that had a handle on it) with water. I tells him the creek ain't over a quarter, en also it rains every year or so, en I points to a water-spout off old Spiegelberg's store, en I also informs him there's a well in the middle o' the Exchange Hotel court-yard, en if he wanted any more information to go over to the newspaper office, as it was my busy day.

"Well, the talk was jest a-flowin 'out o' my little girl; it was all 'bout a *baile* she'd been to the night before, en what such en such a boy said to her, en did I really think he meant it, en I sure did; when the puncher, whose name I afterwards found out was George, passed by with his keg full o' water, headed straight fer the Hanley Saloon. Well, it didn't seem to me he was in there long, fer I was kinder crippled with the talk Miss Dolores was a-handin' me—yes, Dolores was her name; did I tell yer she was a good looker? Well she sure was—when out he comes (en he wasn't breakin' a very straight trail) keg in hand en headed fer the hardware store.

"Dolores had jest got through tellin' me 'bout her second dance when George comes out o' the hardware store with a horse-collar round his neck, a big bundle, en two trace-chains, but still carryin' his two-gallon keg o' water.

Then up the street he goes en into the old Dixon Saloon. I was sure bein' entertained by Miss Dolores en the way she was a tellin' me 'bout her fourth dance, when they swung her so high in the *cutilio* that her little slipper come off en they give it back to her filled with candy en nuts.

"About then old George came out the Dixon Saloon en headed fer Seligman's Dry Goods Store on the corner. I'd jest been told by Dolores that I was the best dancer in town, en wouldn't I take her to the dance to be held at the Barracks that night, en I told her I would. 'A las ocho!' 'Bueno!' 'Adios!' we called after each other as we parted.

"About then I saw George a-comin' out o' Seligman's store, headed fer the Easy Gait Saloon with a new slicker, jumper, en three more packages added to his load, en still carryin' the keg o' water. As it was 'bout time o' day I followed him in, en we had a drink together.

" 'Say, cowboy,' says I, 'why didn't yer wait till yer'd bought all your other tricks before fillin' up your keg with water?'

" 'By hell!' says he, 'I never thought o' that.'

"En as me en another puncher unrolled his beddin' fer him that night he still had a grip on the keg, en it was the first thing he put on his pack-mule as he started fer his ranch in the Estancia Flates country next mornin'.

"Out on the flats nothin' but *chamisa,* alkali, en salt grass in sight, en clouds o' dust blowin' by at fifty miles an hour, don't tend to improve one's temper none, not to any considerable degree. 'Wonder what this country was made fer?' says George to himself. 'Estancia Flats what they call it, but it ain't even that. With their salt lakes en sand hills it never was intended fer a white man anyway. Sha'h! when a cow brute ain't dyin' from the thirst, they're boggin' down in some alkali spring. I'm a-goin' to leave jest as soon as grass gets big enough to travel on, see if I don't.'

"That's the way old George told it to me, who'd lived so long on the alkali flats that his hair had turned white before he was two years old. Our ranches were 'bout twenty miles apart en after this time we'd meet once or twice a year at some round-up where we'd tell our troubles en kinder cheer each other up.

"We'd had an awul drought fer over two years past, en whenever that happened the wells would go dry en everybody would get down in 'em en dig 'em deeper till they got to the water-level aagin. The dry spells had come so often in the last twenty years, that George had dug his well down till it was one o' the deepest on the flats. He was complainin' en kickin' when he was over to the cow-work we had at La Palma.

"He said that the last dirt he threw out o' his well was jest alive with frogs, from little fellers to big ones fourteen or fifteen years old. It seems George had figured out a way to tell their ages which was 'bout like this. He says the little fellers are all 'bout one color, a kind o' brown; when they got to be yearlin's they had a green stripe on each hind leg; en fer every year they got older, they got another stripe; so as the biggest ones had fourteen stripes, they was fifteen years old at least. Well, it seems every one o' those frogs he shoveled out o' that water was dead.

" 'How so?' I asked him.

" 'Well, yer see, it is so doggoned dry in this country that there never has been enough water fer 'em to learn how to swim in, en when that water come into the bottom o' my well they jest naturally drowned to death.

" 'Tell yer, the whole valley's gone to the devil; newcomers from the East comin' in en takin' up all the land, closes'-fisted bunch I ever seen, most of 'em from Illinois; ask yer the biggest fool questions yer ever heard; want ter know when I think it's goin' to rain; did yer ever hear the like? Sundays they all dress up en talk 'bout haw they wish they was all back home. So do I. Seems that's the only thing we do agree 'bout.

" 'I'm jest 'bout as lonesome with this bunch o' newcomers as old Slabs Tyson said the cow-puncher was who'd died en went to Heaven. When he got there, all the men-folks had dress suits on, their vests cut 'way down to their waist-band, en tails to their coats 'most to their heels. All the women had on was lace clothes, en not much o' them.

" 'Well, the old puncher wes jest rigged out regular, en these high-toned folks turned their noses up at him en wouldn't speak. This went on fer some time, till at last one day he saw Saint Peter en asked if he couldn't get a pass to go down to Hell fer a few days en see some o' the boys, as there wasn't anybody where he was that he was acquainted with. As he'd behaved pretty well, Saint Peter gave him a round trip ticket, en off he goes.

" 'Well, the very first person he meets after he arrives was an old puncher from his home town, en he takes en leads him round en shows him the sights. Presently they come to an old barn, en goin' in there they sees 'bout a thousand people all sittin' 'round. They had candles stuck in old bottles en all was a-playin' poker; some of 'em he did know en some he didn't.

" 'Pretty soon the old feelin' come over him, en he jest got to itchin' to horn in, especially when he seen what a little some of 'em did know 'bout the national game. As he didn't have any money en all the boys he knew seemed 'bout broke, he was in a terrible fix. At last after gunnin' round among the different players, he noticed a feller that was dressed up fit to kill, en who seemed kinder out o' place in that bunch, though he sure had a swell stack o' chips in front of him. The puncher got talkin' to the dude en told him 'bout gettin' a ticket from Saint Peter.

good fer a week en after then he'd have to return to Heaven.

" 'One word brought on another, till at last he swapped his return ticket to Heaven fer the dude's pile of chips, sayin' he'd rather live in Hell with a bunch o' punchers than in Heaven with them damn' high-toned dudes. En that's the way I feel 'bout this country en these flat-heeled new-comers.' "

TERRAPINS

"Get down. I see from the brands yer saddle-horses are packin', ye're representin' old man Yost."

"Yep."

That's the way the foreman greeted Hank Mc-Call, who was representing the Double Prod brand, as he rode up to the Bar-W wagon prepared to join in the early spring work.

"Many of our cattle on your range?"

"Yep, quite a few," says Johnson, "en there's no guard to stand tonight, so jest hobble out yer mount en supper will be ready soon."

This puncher McCall who had just ridden up to join the spring work had come from John Yost's ranch over west of the mountains, about a hundred miles from where the Bar-W wagon was then camped, bringing seven horses, or a mount as it was called; and, with nothing else but his outfit and bedding, he was prepared to work the entire round-up or until we had cleaned up, when he would return home with what cattle he had found in the Double Prod or Yost brand.

"How did you leave old man Yost?" asks Johnson. "He must be gettin' pretty old by now. I haven't seen him since we used to live down on the Nuces River in southern Texas, must a been twenty-five years since,—the time he started his trail herd o' land turtles north fer Wyoming. Never heard about that?"

"Nope."

"Well, yer see old man Larrimore en Yost had

been in the cow game in the southern Texas country fer some twenty years ,had built up a good bunch o' brush-cattle, en were jest doin' fine, when at a dance on the Frio River they both goes crazy over the same girl they meets there. Old man Yost was a-settin' her three nights a week en Larrimore the other three, en sometimes the extra night. Well, this went on fer some time, till at last the girl tied up with Larrimore.

"Well, after this happens they don't get along together any more, so they divides up their cattle, en Larrimore starts north up the trail with his share. While the dividin' up is goin' on they gets into a sure-enough man-size fight. Old man Yost bites off the top o' Larrimore's ear, en Larrimore shoots off the end o' Yost's nose. I didn't see it all, as the bronc' I was ridin' jest about then lost his head en swallered himself, but it was sure enough some scrap! Well, after Larrimore had pulled out north with his herd Yost gets to drinkin'. Some say it was 'cause o' the split-up, en some say 'cause Larrimore got the girl. Howsomever that may be, in a few years Yost was plumb busted, en barrin' a bunch o' saddle en stock-horses en his ranch, was all in. Was yer ever down in that southern Texas country?"

"Nope."

"Well, it's pretty much all brush, post oak en such, growin' higher then a man's head on horse-back, so thick yer can hardly ride through it, with every once in a while a little clearin' of a few acres. Well, the cattle o' course go plumb wild; en ridin' out, yer strike the fresh trail of a bunch, en after trailin' 'em en trailin' 'em fer some while yer see your old brush-horse's ears begin to work back en forth.

"Right then yer want to get your line down, fer when the old horse begins to stick his head up, ye're a-comin' to one o' those clearin's en yer got to catch your long-ear before he dives into the brush again. That's why I always claim that yer'll find more good ropers in an outfit in southern Texas than in any other place in the world.

"Well, say, I'm gettin' lost in my story 'bout tellin' yer 'bout old man Yost's trail herd o' turtles, by goin' en tellin' yer how he en old man Larrimore got their start in cattle. Well, while I'm at it I want to say they were both top cow-hands if they did split up over a girl. Well, when Yost got to the end o' his pile he goes up to San Antone fer a trip en meets up with a friend who takes him up to a high-toned restaurant fer a feed, en they sets down to a four-seated table where they was two men already eatin'. Now I happens to be one o' those fellers. The other man looked like he might a been some high-toned eastern drummer; he was a-settin' there sippin' his coffee, readin' his paper, en a-twistin' his mustache. Jest about then in comes the biscuit-shooter en pours a fresh supply o' hot biscuits on the bread platter. Old drummer looks up at Yost en says, 'Can you reach the biscuits?'

"Old Yost, who hadn't liked the looks o' the drummer any more than I had, carefully reaches out his hand, en with the end of his fingers touches the plate o' biscuits, remarkin' in his dry way, 'I jest ken,' after which he withdraws his arm en goes on eatin.' I want to say that was the worst hacked drummer I ever saw.

"Well, Yost's friend orders the grub en they begins on soup. 'Say, Mac,' says Yost to his friend, 'what kind o' soup are we eatin'?' 'That's turtle soup,' says Mac. 'Well, it's sure fine,' says Yost. 'Ought to be,' says his friend; 'costs six bits a dish, en if you ordered it up north it would be about two dollars.' 'Go on,' says Yost. 'It sure would,' says Mac, 'en one turtle makes about twelve dishes.' 'That would make a turtle up there worth about twenty-four dollars,' says Yost. 'Bet your life,' says Mac. 'What kind o' turtles are they?' asks Yost. 'Jest dry land terrapin turtles,' replies Mac. 'Well, I say'—says Yost, but it gave him an idea, en he got to thinkin'.

"A week in San Antone en Yost was glad to get back to his ranch en get his idea to workin'. He got up a mount o' horses en shod them, en with the aid of a couple of his old niggers' sons, started a little horse work, gatherin' all the stock-horses, mares, en colts he could find in his brand. These they drove to San Antone en sold, en Yost found he had enough money to gather en drive his famous herd o' turtles. Now young feller, yer needn't to be a-laughin' fer this is jest what old John Yost did.

"Good luck was with him from the start with the rainy weather settin' in, en as fast as the water would run into the holes that the turtles lived in, out

they would come en sit down to dry off, fer down in
the country I am speakin' of the turtles burrow holes
in the ground in the sand-hills, en live on flies en
such. Well, old Yost en his punchers kept a-ridin'
en a-ridin', each with a gunny-sack tied to his saddle-
horn, pickin' up turles en bringin' 'em in to the
ranch. There they put 'em into a big corral made o'
chicken-wire, en kept 'em till the rainy season was
over en they couldn't catch any more. Then they
walked 'em through a chute en counted 'em, when
they found they had jest fourteen thousand nine hundred en eighty-six. John takes the count over to the
school-teacher en asks him to figure out how much
they would come to at twenty-four dollars a head,
the price he expected to get fer 'em up north. When
the teacher told him it amounted to three hundred en
fifty-nine thousand six hundred en sixty-four dollars,
John like to have died. The expense o' gatherin' the
herd hadn't been so great, but the feedin' of 'em
while in the corral become a serious thing. Old John
had every little nigger within ten miles o' the ranch
catchin' flies en bugs to feed 'em on, en it didn't
ever seem as if they got enough to eat. They always
looked gaunt en drawn, en John thought the sooner
he could hit the trail with 'em the better he would
be off.

"From his experience gained gatherin' these
turtles he knew he would have to keep the herd on
high ground, fer if ever he struck a sandy flat they
would be liable to stampede en try to dig fer them-
selves. He well know if some fifteen thousand tur-

tles all begun diggin' at once, they would be so much dust a-flyin' that they couldn't see to hold 'em. Well, one mornin' early the chuck-wagon pulls out, en John turns the herd out o' the corral, the nigger boys on each side, en old John on the tail end bringin' up the drags. John says they sure was drags, en no use usin' your rope on 'em, fer jest as soon as the turtles saw it comin' down, every head en their four feet would go into their shells, en the whole works would stop.

"About an hour before sundown, Yost had to lope on ahead en overtake the chuck-wagon which he found camped some five miles ahead. Yer see, old Dread the nigger had always driven the chuck-wagon fer a cow outfit, en he didn't know that a herd o' turtles couldn't travel over a few hundred yards a day en consequently at the end o' the first day hadn't gotten outside o' the horse pasture.

"Now the trail drive that Yost aimed to make in order to bring him to where he could market his herd, was about fourteen hundred miles in length. Figurin' that if he made about a quarter of a mile a day it would take him about five thousand six hundred days or some fifteen years, but still havin' that $359,664.00 in mind, he kep' a-goin'.

"When late fall came it began to freeze every night, en the herd got so restless they could hardly keep 'em on the bed ground, and to keep 'em from stampedin' when night came on they would turn the turtles on their backs. Unfortunately Yost found after a little experimentin', that when layin' on their backs they would kick their legs all night long, en would be so tired when mornin' came that they could hardly travel at all. Then one mornin' Yost had to leave several hundred turtles behind, as they had their feet frost-bitten; en the weather gettin' colder en colder, he decided to go into camp fer the winter. Huntin' him up a nice sandy bottom, he hired a ranchman who owned a big plow to plow him some furrows—en do yer know every last turtle when night come on crawled into those furrows en layed down. After the turtles all got nicely bedded down Yost had the farmer drag the loose dirt over the top of 'em, en he now had his herd safe fer the winter. Yost next bought some hay en grain fer his horses en grub fer his outfit, moved into a dugout, en prepared to spend the winter.

"He now had a long wait before the spring opened up so he could again hit the trail.

"Winter time on the plains o' the Panhandle in Texas is liable to be cold—in fact, always is. Comin' out o' southern Texas where it was warm, old Yost en his darkies, except fer the dugout, like to have froze to death. Somehow, in some way they managed to tough it through, though old Dread the darkey remarked, 'Boss, dis is do out-freezin'est country in de whole world.''

"When the frost came out o' the ground in the spring, green grass soon appeared en the buzzin' of insects told 'em they would soon again be on the trail. After plowin' out his turtles Yost put 'em on the trail; but they traveled very slow fer he found that the herd, owin' to the innumerable number o' small turtles which had arrived durin' the winter, had doubled in size en consequently was harder to handle. This, although a seemin' drawback regardin' drives, meant a much larger return when the herd was marketed. The herd had already swam several rivers without any loss, en the great Red River which was the next one to be met with held no terrors to old Yost.

"The news concernin' old Yost's herd o' turtles bein' driven up the trail had o' course spread all over Texas en preceded him as far north as the Kansas line. Now it happened that old man Larrimore had settled on the banks o' Red River en had heard o' Yost en his herd o' dry land turtles, en that they not only was on their way but was daily expected to arrive on Red River. En Larrimore after all these years had never forgiven Yost fer havin' bit off the top of his ear, even if he had won from him the girl they was both courtin'. Followin' receipt o' the news o' Yost's expected arrival, Larrimore schemed how he could get even with him fer the loss o' half his hearer, en though Iarrimore had shot off the end o' Yost's nose in the scrap, he could never quite forgive him.

"On July the fourth Yost found himself en herd on the banks o' the Red River with the turtles all nicely strung out fer the water. I know the fourth was the date, as fer years afterwards Yost would never go to any Fourth o' July celebration en always cussed the day en the man who invented it.

Well, one o' the boys who had been workin' in the lead o' the herd rode up to Yost en reported that he had seen a man in a row-boat monkeyin' about a log or a stump that seemed fast in the middle o' the river. As he watched the man in the boat, he noticed him lean over the log en place a pan on it en afterwards somethin' round en black which looked in the distance like a turtle. However, as the man en boat had disappeared towards the other bank o' the river he could not positively say what he *had* been doin'.

"Presently the herd o' turtles in a long line enters the water en swum along fine till the lead turtle come abreast o' the log in the middle o' the stream. Suddenly Yost, who had been watchin' 'em close, saw somethin' dive off o' that log, en every last turtle in that herd dived after it.

"Well, with their increase, somethin' over a half a million dollars' worth o' good turtles was lost fer all time. En as Yost expected to be fourteen years more on the trail, he had lost also the turtles' natural increase fer *that* time, which Yost figured would be worth at least sixty million dollars that he could count. Jest because Yost's old pardner Larrimore had put a divin' mud turtle on a log, to get even with old Yost fer bitin' off his ear."

McQUEEN'S HORSE SALE

We'd had the wagon camped at the rock crossing on the Pecos a couple of days, the boys working both sides of the river, and at about two o'clock, my horse going lame, I quit the drive and came in. No one was there but old Sanders the cook, so as I was eating me a little snack I saw a man riding in from the west and leading a horse. I didn't pay much attention till he got up pretty close, when I saw it was old Tobe Barber, who had quit two days before to go to Texas where his grandmother, as he told me, was very sick, riding his old smoke horse and leading a big fat mare followed by a colt. As he got near I could see that he was loaded. When he pulled up to the wagon I noticed a bottle of champagne sticking out of each saddle pocket, and tied around his horse's neck were a lot of table napkins carefully knotted together so they made a kind of necklace.

"Hello, Tobe, you made a fast trip to Texas. Must have been ridin' some," was what I said as he rode up. "How's your grandmother?"

"Some improved," he said, "and she sent you this," said Tobe in a very drunken voice, handing me a bottle of champagne out of his saddle-pocket.

"Doctor says she may croak any minute, but still there's hope." And he took a good stiff drink out of a silver flask which he produced from his hip-pocket.

"Where'd you get that millionaire's whiskey bottle from, Tobe?"

"Up at shale."

"Did you get that mare and colt up at the 'shale' too?"

"Yep," says Tobe, "sure did".

I tried to get some more news; but what Tobe had had to drink up at the 'shale', as he called it, added to the heat of the sun, put him past speech; and unrolling his bed for him I soon had him fast asleep.

In several different places lately I had seen notices concerning a sale of horses to be held at Mc-Queen's, but had paid no particular attention till the arrival of Tobe reminded me that the sale had already been held. Next day I had to go after the mail. I learned at the P. O. that the train was several hours late, but as I expected a letter of instructions from the supreme boss I decided to wait.

Part of the following as to what happened at the sale, I got from a young man I met at the station and who was living with McQueen. The rest just trickled out of the boys from time to time during the round-up. It seems that McQueen, who had come from the old country some years before, had bought up a lot of trotting-mares and started raising good stock. After he had raised a number of yearling and two-year-old colts, he thought he would do as is customary in the old country—hold a sale of all young stock on hand.

Now in the cow country a trotting bred horse is about as useful for running cattle as a sewing machine is to a dog-catcher, but nevertheless that sound of a breakfast for everybody, free, caught the waddies' eyes, so, though no one was expected till after ten o'clock as soon as the sun got up the punchers began to arrive. They were received by McQueen with his aides, dressed in English riding clothes, little rattan sticks in their hands and everything complete as they would appear at a regular English horse-sale.

The boys arrived, rode over to the corral, tied their horses, and looked the stock over; and as they went from stall to stall they connected up with a bottle which was passed around, promiscuous like, by one of the attendants. This, I suppose, was done under the mistaken impression that the better the prospective purchasers felt, the more liberal would be their patronage.

Things were rocking along smoothly when McQueen himself happened over to the corrals to welcome his guests. The first contingent to arrive were some eleven cow-punchers who, through the hospitality of Mac's lieutenants, were all fairly shiny.

"Hello, Mac," they all saluted him in chorus; and Clabe, who took on himself to be chief spokesman, informed Mac that they had been holding a meeting and had elected him a member of the Cow-punchers' Union, and now all that remained before he became a real member was the initiation. Mac in a joking way agreed. "Well", said Clabe, "the first order is fer you ter take a drink with each o' your brethern, en as I'm the Grand Rope-twister, yer can start with me."

Well, as Bill Minnix afterwards remarked, takin' eleven drinks, one after another, each with a different brother don't tend ter sober a man none.

After the last pledge, someone pulled a fuzzy-guzzy out of his pocket and proposed a game. Now to the uninitiated I wish to explain that a fuzzy-guzzy is a small top with four sides, on which are marked A. N. W. L. (All, Nothing, Win, Lose). The boys spread a slicker on the ground, and as the game was a new one to Mac he fell for it and fell hard.

As Al afterwards explained to me, he "never saw a man who could spin as many L's runnin' with never another letter," in his life. But after he had donated all his ready cash it seems that Tobe won his silver flask, and Tom Gray his watch. He then proposed a horse-race. Now I have known cow-punchers to get loaded, even when they had to fill their own glasses, but when a bunch of them are so situated that there are several flunkies fillin' glasses for them! (Kid of mine, hold your tongue!) Well, Mac agreed to run a big fat mare he owned, named Lady Something-or-other, against Tobe's smoky horse, a half mile, horse for horse, colt thrown in, and while the horses were being saddled he told one of his flunkies to bring six quarts of champagne.

"Say," said Al afterwards, "I never had drunk any o' that stuff before, en it sure does funny things to yer. About half a bottle made old Long Hayes get up en preach as good a sermon as ever I heard at a Texas camp meetin', made old Livingston tell how sorry he felt fer our old range-boss, that he had ter work fer a living, (him gettin' twice as much as Liv-

ingston was), made Dick Bass go over en hug a fat
Jersey calf, en console with it en tell it its mammy
ought ter be ashamed of itself fer not givin' more
milk, en she a four gallon cow; en by the time the
horses was brought they had to wake me up, fer there
I sat a-huggin' old Vick, the homeliest man on the
river.''

Now out on his front lawn Mac had a lot of
small tables put together with cloths over them, mak-
ing one table about fifty feet long, all laid out in
style, glass, silverware, and everything in the world
to eat and drink. Out in front of this was a small
oval track, which was used to exercise his trotting
stock and also as a turn-around place in front of the
house, with roads branching off the central track in
several directions. As the roads away from the house
were not very good, almost all the exercise his horses
got was around this little track, and his nags knew
every crook and turn like a book.

It was decided to start the race about two hundred
yards south of the back stretch of the track, then
enter the back stretch, keep on straight past the curve
in the track, and finish up at an old post which
marked one of the corners of the ranch. Well, after
Mac had got his gloves on, the horses went to the
starting place, one of the flunkies went over and
dropped a handkerchief, and away they went.

''Say'', said Bill Minnix who told me this part,
''that old mare sure could run. When she struck the
track on the far side she was at least four lengths
ahead, en the colt a-runnin' by her side. They sure

had Tobe on Smoky whippin' en spurrin'.''

But jest as soon as the mare struck the track she quit runnin' en settled down into a trot, en all Mac's urgin' couldn't make her change her gait. Tobe soon caught en passed her en pulled up at the finish alone, the mare en Mac goin' on in grant style around the turn en never stoppin' till she brought up at the tables.

''Come on, everybody, till I explain,'' says Mac, so we all joined him en the flunkies opened up a few more bottles.

''Now I say, old chaps'' says Mac, ''I hardly call that a fair test don't yer know, en with all of your permissions let's try again.''

They did; same results; more bottles. I believe they would a been runnin' that race over yet if Mac hadn't got so drunk he couldn't ride, when he admits at last he had got beat.

After Mac got so he would slide out of his chair under the table, the boys apparently picked him up and set him among the dishes and eats. He proposed to sing, and the boys certainly helped him. Then he got solemn as a judge and insisted on giving each puncher some little ''souvenir'', as he called it, of one of the happiest days of his life. He gave away all the silverware, napkins, everything to eat, and at last everything to drink. March said, ''When the boys left him he was a-sittin' in the middle o' the table, a carving knife in one hand en a huge fork in the other, beatin' time on the salad bowl en singin' 'God Save McQueen.' ''

THE BURRO AND THE GIANT POWDER

Having come in the trail of a little bunch of cattle which he turned into the day herd, Amos rode up to the chuck-wagon and got down off his horse.

"Hello Amos," called out old John the cook, "come down the cañon?"

"Yeah."

"Didn't make it in from Lone Tree today, did yer?"

"No, I stayed all night at Jim's en Neal's camp."

"Well get around. There's meat, beans, en bread in the oven, en some fresh coffee I jest made. Fly at it."

"Bueno," said Amos.

"What's the news over Lone Tree way?" asked old John.

"Nothing much, but they had some excitement at Jim's en Neal's place."

"How so?"

"Well, it seems a few days ago the two old fellers takes their burros en goes on down to Lone Tree ter lay in supplies so they could finish up some work on their mining claims. Before leaving their claims, Jim had made out a list o' supplies they would need, en gave it to Neal. The list, besides provisions, included several rolls of fuse, some caps, en fifty pounds o' giant powder.

"When the two pardners got to town, Neal met an old friend en commenced to liquor up. Pretty soon, knowin' he wasn't in no shape to go shoppin', he hunted up Jim en told him if he would buy what was needed en load it on the burros, he would start late that evening fer camp. A couple of hours before sundown, Jim hunted up his pardner, helped him out o' town, en put him on the trail with the three burros laden down with provisions en supplies fer the mine.

"Two of the burros was old-timers which Jim and Neal had owned fer the last ten years. The third burro was a three-year-old they had raised around camp, a regular pot-licker en camp-robber; eat anything; had been spoiled en petted by the two old fellers ever since at two weeks of age its mother had died. Whenever Baby, as the two pardners called it, got frightened, or dogs or boys bothered it, it would run to whichever o' the pardners happened to be nearest, fer protection.

"Well, the trail Neal was on followed Percha Creek, which heads on the northern side of old Baldy Mountain. Stumbling along behind his burros, a-smokin' his pipe, Neal would from time to time sing a song tell a story, en laugh, like all old prospectors will do who have spent their lives in the mountains alone. After an hour on the trail it began to grow dark en Neal decided he had better camp for the night. Presently, comin' to a little flat by the side of a stream, he stopped the burros en commenced to unpack.

"The two older burros were loaded with provisions of all kinds but no powder, fuse, or caps, en as he hobbled 'em out Neal told 'em what he thought of his pardner fer givin' the dangerous part o' their supplies to a young burro like Baby, who might get scared at something run against a tree, explode the giant powder, en blow everything to hell. 'Well', thinks Neal as he approached Baby, 'next time I'll do the packing myself.' Baby, when Neal approached, commenced smellin' in his pockets fer anything he might find, Neal meanwhile unfastenin' the flap o' the canvas pack saddle bag en feelin' inside.

"Well, the first thing his hand touched was a roll of fuse, en this he took out. While he was again reachin' in with one hand en holdin' up the flap o' the saddle bag with the other, a puff o' wind carries the ashes of his pipe inside, en a second later the fuse was lighted. Well, as the smoke rolled out o' the saddle pockets, Neal loses his head, en instead o' tryin' to jerk the burnin' fuse out o' the pockets, he starts ter run.

"Now a roll of fuse, dependin' on its size, will burn fer an hour or more, but Neal could only remember that he hadn't found no giant powder en caps in the other burros packs. He knew they must be in this one, en he thought only of when the burning fuse would light 'em. Well, he simply flew.

"Baby, all unconscious of any trouble, stood still, a-watchin' the flyin' Neal, wonderin' when he would come back to finish the unpackin' en turn her loose so she could have her evening roll. While turnin' he head to kill a fly, Baby suddenly saw the cloud o' smoke comin' out o' the saddle pocket. Not knowin' of course what the trouble was, but smellin' danger, Baby started fer the only protection she knew when in trouble, that of her master.

"Startin' in a walk, she soon turned into a trot, en as her movements fanned the flames, she began ter gallop. Presently she made the turn of the cañon around which Neal had disappeared, en speedin' along she pretty near caught up to him. But Neal sees her comin' en redoubles his efforts to get away from what he was blame sure was instant death.

"Dodgin' among boulders, in and out of arroyos, around the big pines, goes Neal, with Baby all the while close at his heels. As the darkness increased, the burnin' only shone brighter, en Neal begun callin' on his Saints to protect him; though as the burro kept at his heels, Neal commences ter suspect that not a single Saint was inclined to interfere en save him. Finally, gettin' desperate, he roars at the burro, 'As yer love me get away, yer devil!' but his voice only seemed to bring Baby nearer.

"Well, with Baby matchin' stride with him, straight up the cañon goes Neal, while mile after mile the burro he-haws after him, till at last, thoroughly overcome, Neal falls exhausted.

"Next mornin' his pardner, Jim on his way to the mine, found the two burros Neal had unpacked, but he couldn't find no signs o' Neal or Baby anywheres. But followin' the cañon's course, he presently come on Baby contentedly grazin', while not far away at the foot of a tree lay Neal to all appearance as good as dead, goes up to him real cautious en gives the sole of his boot a kick, whereupon the corpse raised up.

"Neal, seein' Jim en the burro at the same time, yells, 'Get that damn' burro away, or we'll all be blown to hell!'

"Well, Jim's glance at the charred saddle-bag told him the story.

" 'Don't worry about the burro, Neal. When I packed the burros I forgot ter put the caps en giant powder in 'em, en I brought 'em up with me this mornin'. ' "

THE PUNCHER AND THE NUGGET

"Hello, Chalk, which way?"

"I'm goin' over to the Sacramento outfit. I've got a job goin' up the trail with the herd."

"Well, it's gettin' kind o' late. Yer better unsaddle en stay all night, 'less yer want to make a dry camp."

"Well, I believe I will."

"Turn your horse into the horse-pasture en come on in. I'm short on augerin."

"Where's your old side-pardner, Chalk?"

"Which one?"

"Why, old Tom Beasley."

"I left him in El Paso 'bout a week ago, but I've heard he left there since. Yer heard about him en Henry Heap? No? Maybe yer heard Tom had been workin' east over here on the state line, helpin' Jack's Jax drill a well? They was workin' there about half way between the Alamo and Cornudas, and some south, on the road to Crow Flat.

"Well, Tom was gettin' good wages en held down his job fer about a year, saved up his money and acted real good.

"One day a feller come into camp a-foot. No one there but Tom; everyone else had gone to the mountains to haul down a log cabin that they wanted to set up. This feller said that durin' the night his horses had run off. Well, there he was with a family, a dry camp, en no horses, en as he come from the East he didn't even know how to follow their trail. Well Tom he saddles the stranger up a horse, gets himself another one, en pulls out. Directly they comes to the wagon en Tom goes to cuttin' sign. They were big eastern horses en all shod, en the trail bein' clear, Tom lopes along on it, but presently notices that there is only tracks o' one horse. He follows that track till sun-down, en at last runs onto one o' the horses and brings him back, then hitches his old saddle horse en the one he found to the wagon, en pulls the outfit down to the well-rig where they could have water to camp on.

"Well, next mornin' Tom saddles up again en trails the other fool horse who'd gone off in another direction, en about night time gets back to the wagon with him.

"Well, the feller didn't have any money, en Tom didn't want any, but he give Tom (as he said, to remember him by) a big gold nugget he'd brought from the Klondike when he was there some years before.

"Spring comes on en Tom's back, I guess, commenced to itch. Anyway he got the movin' fever, drew his money en pulled out fer El Paso, told old Jack's Jax he'd got a letter from home en had to go. Funny, a puncher never will own up he just wants to lay off en get drunk.

"Well, the second night Tom rolls into El Paso, en it didn't take him long to hunt up the Wigwam, en Astor House.

"Tom lays around town fer a couple o' weeks, playin' Monte en drinkin' his share, attendin' all the

Mexican bailes en takin' in the bull-fights across the river, till his money begin to get low.

"Standin' one night in the doorway o' the Astor House he overheard two men beside him talkin' about a man who was passin'. One, it seems, asks the other who the man was. The other man says, 'That's Henry Heap.'

" 'What does he do?' asks the first party.

" 'Don't do nothin', but gets well paid fer it.'

" 'What's his graft?' asks number one.

" 'Oh, he's just a private policeman en bank watchman,' replies his friend. 'He makes good money watchin' the bank en puts almost all of it in fool prospect holes. He's nuts about minin'.'

"A few nights after Tom had heard these fellers talkin' en his pile had been cut down ter a few dollars in silver, he sees Henry go into a saloon, en directly Tom follows him. Tom was pretty drunk but could still navigate.

" 'Come on everybody, en have a drink with me,' says Tom, throwin' down on the bar what silver en other trinkets he had in his pocket.

"Henry among others stepped up en ordered his drink, when he noticed the gold nugget a layin' on the bar among the change.

" 'Hello,' says he to Tom, 'what's this?'

" 'I don't know,' says Tom.

" 'Where'd you get it?' says Henry.

" 'Oh, out between here and the mountains.'

" 'My horse got a stone in his shoe en I got down to knock it out en found this on the ground.

"Henry got his magnifyin' glass out en looked the nugget all over, then called Tom aside. 'Say,' says he, 'My name's Henry Heap. Do yer know where there's any more o' this rock?'

" 'Sure,' says Tom, 'there's acres of it out there.'

" 'Do yer mind if I break a piece o' this off and have it assayed?'

" 'Help yerself,' says Tom. 'Take all yer want; I can get plenty more of it.'

"Next mornin' Tom just did have the price of a breakfast en saunterin' down the street runs into Henry.

" 'Say Tom,' says Henry, who'd gotten his returns on the assay, 'how much will yer take to show me the place where yer got that piece of rock?'

" 'Oh, I don't know,' says Tom. 'Was it any account?'

" 'Oh, pretty fair,' says Henry, who didn't tell Tom it had assayed over forty thousand dollars to the ton.

" 'Well, I tell yer,' says Tom, 'I got to stay in town a few days longer, en whenever I fix to go it won't cost yer nothin' to come along.'

" 'Well, how are yer fixed fer cash?' says Henry.

" 'I'm about broke,' says Tom, 'en need a few things at the store.'

"Well, they goes over to the Golden Eagle en Tom gets a whole new outfit, orders a pair o' shop boots, en paid up corral charges on the saddle horse fer a week ahead, en got a twenty-dollar gold piece to keep him runnin'.

"Tom told me he never did intend to hang it onto Henry, but when he wouldn't tell him how much the nugget assayed, and showed he was tryin' to get the best of him, Tom decided to make him pay. Well, every day or two Henry would come through with five or ten till at last he decided, on account o' Tom puttin' off the time of startin' so often, to quit.

"When the story got around town, everyone who'd meet Henry would pick up a stone, en rushin' up to him (always waitin' till he was in a crowd) sing out, 'Say Henry, can yer tell me how much this runs in gold?' en to get rid o' the joshin' he'd stand treat fer the whole crowd."

THE COUNTERFEITER

"Come on, Walker, get your nose out o' that grub pile, it's your turn. Yer got your choice—to sing a song, tell a yarn, or dance, or over the wagon-tongue you go."

This was Johnson, the foreman, speaking to one of the stray punchers representing the Lightning-Rod brand.

"Well here's at yer," replied Walker. "You boys remember old Steve Mendenthal over on the Pecos River?"

"Yeah," was the general response.

"Well, you recollec' Steve wasn't very strong on education, specializin' most particular on mules— could tell yer just exactly how many he had after someone else had counted 'em but not before.

"Well, Steve had two kids, en as he had no education himself, decided that they should have the best that money could buy. After they had learned everything the teachers in the high-school knew, Steve sends 'em east. I don't jest remember where the girl was sent, but as it's the boy I'm goin' to tell yer about, I remember he went to Yale College. I know that's right, fer the old man when he had his job contractin' on the Pecos Railroad used to bring Fred's (yep, that was the boy's name) letters over fer me to read to him. Yer can bet every one o' them started with a 'Dear Dad,' en ended with a 'Please send a check,' which the old man always had me make out en put in the envelope with his reply. My, how he used to brag about that boy, en what did I think of his hand-writing? It sure enough was jest like printin', about the finest I ever saw.

"Well, I guess it was about some four years after Fred went east, that he come back with what he called his sheep-skin. However, it was a big piece o' heavy paper, en written in some foreign language, I remember, it had 'Sic Temper Tyrants' on it, which Fred told me, interpreted into he-English, meant he had graduated with honors.

"Well, he sure was a smart kid, en could beat anyone at the Last Call Saloon a-playin' pool. Finally the old man got him a job as timekeeper on the railroad, but as it was pretty tough weather down on the Pecos in the winter, what with sandstorms en one thing en another, Fred quit. Then the old man starts him in a store. When he had run that a while he got married, en old Steve thought he had him anchored fer life. But no, he was the most restless kid yer ever saw, always thinkin' o' the good times he'd had back at college, en talkin' about the Beetle Fly, or some secret society he used to belong to, en wishin' he was back there again.

"Now what I'm tellin' yer about happened fifteen years ago; least, that's when Fred disappeared. Well, no one knew what become of him en finally he was jest forgotten.

"After we broke up work last fall I takes a job goin' down to the City o' Mexico with six carloads o' fine horses. After layin' around El Paso a month, I was flat broke, en I was mighty glad to get the job, as I figured to winter down there where it was warm on what money I got out o' the trip. That's the place to winter, boys; a hat, a blanket to wrap around yer, en drinks a *claco* a chance, which in our money is about a cent en a helf. En girls—!''

"Oh, shut up about the girls, Walker, en go on with your yarn.''

"Well, after the longest railroad journey in the world, I got to the Ciudad de Mexico, as they call it, en hunted up the man who was to receive the horses. Talk about polite people, those Mexicans down there are out o' reach of any others in the world. The man who received the horses thought he could talk English, en I thought I could talk Spanish, but *no bueno*. As a compromise he steers me over to the American Bar, he orderin *tragitos* in Spanish, while I calls fer mine in American.

"Say, you boys ought o' seen that hotel en bar. En who do yer suppose I met while down there? Yer couldn't guess in a lifetime. Well I'll tell yer, old high-hocked Rogers, en Shorty Mann.''

"Rogers of the movies?''

"Yep, the same. Well, as I was a-sayin' I was a-passin' one night along to Don Simplimento's house —he was the feller who received the horses en that I went to work fer, payin' me two hundred dollars a month in gold to keep his horses from gettin' sick; did yer ever hear the like? Well, when goin' to his house I passed a little cantina with the door wide open on the street, en there lined up to the bar was two men en two girls. Course that's usual in Mexico, but what made me stop was that they was a-singin' in real El Paso English. In I steps, fer Americans ain't so frequent in Mexico City as the advertisin' people would have you believe. I sidles up along next to 'em en joins in the song. Presently they closes their mouth en wants to know who hired me. 'Bout then we reckonizes en grabs each other en give a fine imitation of a Navajo Shimmy.

"We has a few drinks, en the boys introduced me to their wives. I notices the girl standin' next to me has one foot on the bar-rail en the other on the floor, en seems to be standin' up real straight. When the other girl turns around I notices she is a blinkey, only has one eye. Well, we was all so glad to see each other that we jest kep' on orderin' 'em.

Seems Rogers en Mann had been in the City about a year, en had both married daughters o' neighborin' ranchmen who was pretty well fixed, the boys holdin' down jobs as foremen o' their father-in-law's ranches, en they were now in town fer Fiesta Week. Rogers confided in me that o' course his wife had only one eye, but she at least had two good legs; while Shorty Mann told me to notice his wife's beautiful eyes, en although one of her legs was shorter 'n the other he didn't marry her to run foot races with her, nohow.

"Well, things rocked with me fine; not a horse got sick; me gettin' my money regular, en Don Simplimento payin' my board at the finest hotel in town. The Don who ran the big hotel where I lived, en I, got awful thick. Seems he always took his drinks at the bar the same hours as I did, usually from seven to twelve, but in case we missed each other we always waited for the other to appear, which would be some time between one en six. This Don Felipe, who ran the hotel could talk pretty good spick English, except when he got excited, when overboard he would fall en you couldn't understand a word he said.

"I was jest comin' in the front door o' the hotel one evenin' (havin' been away all day with my boss) when Don Felipe rushed up en grabbin' me by the shoulder says: 'You not know este son-of-a-gun Señor Mendenthal? El Señor Federico con el bigote black, el es a damn' ladrón! I catch him, I kill him, hell I hate him too much! Come, I show you, he no eat two, three days, carambas!'

"Don Felipe leadin', I follows him to the door of a room on the ground floor o' the hotel, where, piled against it, was numbers o' trays each containin' a ample meal fer a hungry man. Pointin' at the trays Don Felipe threw up both hands. 'Vamoosed, blowed, gone, what you call skeeped! Ten thousand dollars gone, I hate him too much!' We opened the door en steppin' over the trays o' food entered the room.

"Except fer the furniture the only things in the room was a grip en a dirty collar. Seizin' these Don Felipe jumps on 'em. 'Carambas' en 'ladrón', was all I could get out of him. He jest was too mad to talk. 'For what you no tell me where he lived? I find, I pull hees damn' body from hees nose! Carambas!'

"Well, I met Don Felipe some days afterwards.

By then he'd gotten over his mad en could again speak English, en he told me this story of Fred Mendenthal.

"Mendenthal had arrived in Mexico City from the North about a month before I got there, had engaged a swell room, en promptly every week paid his bill. Don Felipe had noticed that Señor Federico, as he called him, kept his room durin' the day, though burnin' a light en keepin' his shades drawn down, but at night he was always away from the hotel.

"Well Don Felipe presently became acquainted with his guest en asked him one day what his business was, en after a while Fred told Don Felipe if he would promise to keep secret anything he told him he probably could make him a lot o' money. Don Felipe goes with Fred to his room, where he sees littered on a big writing-table bottles of various kinds of ink, pens, pencils, glass plates, magnifyin' glass, en two five-dollar Bank o' Mexico bills. An old one was fastened to the table with thumb-tacks, while jest below it a new bill was fixed in the same way.

"All of a sudden Fred says, 'Don Felipe, I am a professional forger en one of the best in the world.' En pullin' the thumb-tacks out o' the bills he hands 'em to him to examine. 'The old bill,' says Fred, 'was my pattern; the new one is the copy from it which I have jest finished. Now Don Felipe, if you can keep your mouth shut we can make a lot o' money by formin' a partnership. I'll make the money en you get rid of it by turnin' it into your bank with the cash you take in every day. Now I tell you what to do. Take this five-dollar bill I've jest made, put it in with the other paper yer took in, in yer business, en turn it in to your bank as a deposit. If by any chance the bank spots it, you jest say you received it in the course o' business, en they will deduct it from your account, en nothin' more will be said. Don Felipe,' he says, 'you can't squeal on me, fer as I have no more counterfeit money in my possession, even if yer did tell the police I made that five-dollar bill, you could not prove it.

" 'Bueno,' says Don Felipe, 'I'll do it—deposit this bill with my cash en see how it goes.'

"Now Don Felipe was a crafty old bird, en when he made his deposit at the bank that afternoon he kept the five-dollar bill separate from his other money, en handin' it to the bank teller says, 'I have a five-dollar bill here that I got in my hotel business, en as I don't know if it's good or not I wish yer'd look at it.'

"The teller takes the bill, puts it under a magnifyin' glass en returns it to Don Felipe, sayin', 'I wish I had a million dollars like it. Yes Don Felipe, it's absolutely good.'

"Well, Don Felipe returns to the hotel delighted with what he had found out. He found Fred sittin' in the lounge, en callin' him into a private room tells him what the banker had said, meanwhile handin' him two dollars en fifty cents in silver as his share of the transaction. Don Felipe ordered the waiter to bring drinks, en was very much wrought up over the outlook o' gettin' hold o' some easy money.

"Well, Fred explained that it was jest as much work to make a five-dollar bill as it was a ten thousand one, en the only reason he had not make a handsomer bill was that he was almost broke, en didn't have a larger one as a pattern. If Don Felipe would get one, in three day's time he would reproduce it exactly, en they would again divide the profits.

"The followin' Day, Don Felipe brought Fred a ten thousand-dollar National Bank note, en he immediately retired to his room with it, leavin' instructions that fer three days he wasn't to be disturbed, but that the bell-boy could leave a tray o' food occasionally at his door, en he would eat when he wanted.

"Three days passed en no signs of Fred, until at last Don Felipe gets impatient en knocks on the door. Repeated knockin' bringin' no response, he calls a bell boy en goes in with a pass key. Well, there's only an empty grip, a dirty collar, en an open window to show Don Felipe what become of Don Federico, the ten thousand-dollar bill, en his one en only attempt to get rich quick."

CURIOUS WOMEN

By N. HOWARD THORP

"Pull Slick out o' that bed en let's hear what he's got ter say."

"No pullin' needed. I'm comin', but I ain't the bearer of any news. Never told a story in my life; as I'm a strong church member I don't dance; en my throat is so sore eatin' what the cook calls chile gravy en I call dynamite, that I can't sing," replied Slick to the foreman's invitation to display his talents.

"Slick," said Johnson, "the wagon-tongue is jest a-groanin' fer yer company, en there lays a pair o' freshly greased chaps, en here is four punchers a-dyin' ter use them. What de yer say?"

"By hell!" says Slick. "Well, boys, if you'll be satisfied with the oldest story in the world, one my grandad heard from his grandad, why here goes.

"Seems the old man lived on a street in a little town back east where all the houses looked pretty much alike. Each house was built up two-storey-high, had a little yard in front en rear, en neat little picket fences. He says most everybody fished fer a livin' en was mostly good church members. Seems that all that wasn't fishermen was jest tramps en bums en wouldn't speak to a job if they met it in the road. Some o' the people would give them a hand-out, en some would give 'em hell fer askin fer it. Well, in one o' these neat little houses lived a widder woman known among her neighbors as a tale-bearer, a gossip, en the most curious clothes-rack a-livin'.

Every tramp knew there was no use goin' ter her cage fer anything, so they left her mostly alone.

"But one day a new bum struck town, en not knowin' the lay o' things butted right into this old hen's home, en when the back door was opened got the tongue-lashing of his life. Now this tramp was no ordinary bum but was fer the time bein' up against it. Formerly he had been with a circus as barker fer a side-show, had been a three-shell artist, sleight-o'-hand man, en he knew human nature en its weaknesses out en in.

" 'So yer won't give a poor man who is in desperate circumstances a bite to eat, lady?' says the tramp to her when he had a chance ter get a word in.

" 'No, you big strong man,' says she, 'you ought ter be ashamed o' yerself, beggin'. Why don't yer go to work?'

" 'Well, lady,' says the tramp, 'if yer won't give me something to eat, may I have that broken board en those few chips a-lyin' over there?'—pointing to a corner o' the yard.

" 'Well,' replies the old jane, 'if I give them to yer what are yer goin' to do with 'em?'

" 'Why lady, as I said I'm awful hungry, en if you'll give 'em ter me I want to build a fire en make some rock soup.'

" 'Rock soup?' says the old reptile; 'how are yer goin' to do that?'

" 'Well, lady, I'll need this old kettle here on the porch, en then I'll show you.'

"The tramp then takes the kettle, fills it with

water from the faucet, builds a fire, en sets it to
boil—the water, not the fire—with the old girl all
the time a-follerin' round en gawpin'. Next the
tramp hunts around among the different piles o'
rock along the fence, tryin' ter pick out a rock that
will suit. The first one he selects he carries over ter
the faucet en carefully washes en dries on his coat,
but after examining it closely throws it back in the
pile again. The old woman is still on his trail, back
en forth, a-watchin' every move he makes. After
choosein' en throwin' back about a dozen rocks he
at last decides on a black one, en carefully washin' it
puts it in the pot o' boiling water.

" 'Well, that beats anything I ever saw,' says
the by-now-worried woman. 'Do you mean ter tell
me it makes a differenec what kind of a stone yer
use to make your soup?'

" 'Most certainly, lady. A little slip at this
junction of the decocting might entirely destroy the
inanimate molecules which constitute the hiatus of
this compound. All constitutional parts must, in
their perfect blendin' o' form, color, en flavor, lend
an air of verisimilitude to the whole. En were I ter
err in the slightest degree in judgment or otherwise,
the en-tire experiment would be rendered non compus
mentis.'

" 'Land's sakes!' was the old hen's reply.

" 'En now, lady, as yer seem interested in my
demonstration which previously I have been extreme-
ly reticent in givin', I will ask that you bring me a
couple of onions—preferably white ones.'

"So mumblin' to herself that the man must be crazy the old she-serpent goes to the kitchen en returns with the onions like he told her.

" 'Will the rock cook ter pieces?" asked Old Curiosity.

" 'Sure,' says the barker, 'but in order ter properly dissolve it we must subject it to certain acids, the most potent en powerful of which is your-an-assic acid, which is instantly evolved by combining with the ingredients already in the pot a good portion each o' beef en potatoes. If yer will kindly procure me these—say two or three pounds o' raw beef, a dozen potatoes, en a spoonful o' salt?'

"These bein' brought en placed in the pot, old lanternjaw ran ter the fence where she saw a neighbor a-hangin' her arms, en invited her in to see the wonderful demonstration o' convertin' a rock into palatable food. Meanwhile the barker was goin' on with his line o' talk: 'Chemistry teaches us that all organic matter is soluble. This fact the alchemists of olden days always bore in mind while convertin' the baser metals into gold. Now, ladies, if yer will kindly bring some soup-dishes en spoons, also some bread en butter, I will generously allow yer to pass judgment on whether or not I have produced a palatable soup from a plain rock.'

" 'Now, young man,' says Old Curiosity, 'let me have that spoon. I want ter stir in that pot en find out whether or not that rock has been cooked ter pieces.'

" 'Certainly,' replies the barker, 'but as there

is such a quantity o'soup in the pot, I suggest yer bring the plates, en after fillin' 'em there will be so much less in the container that you can the more readily see. So hurry up en we will let the soup simmer.'

" 'Gosh,' thought the barker, 'close shave, that.' En a few minutes later the woman returned with soup dishes, bread, en butter. After ladlin' the plates full the inquisitive one seizes the big spoon en stirs en stirs, but wonder o' wonders there wasn't no rock in the pot, not even a pebble. Well, while they're all a-settin' enjoyin' the big meal o' several helps o' soup en big slices o' bread-en-butter, the two dumbfounded females goes ter heapin' compliments on the barker en tells him what a special flavor the rock gives to the soup en how wonderful he was ter have dissolved the rock, 'even with your-an-ass-ic acid. Doesn't it taste a little like sparrer-grass, that acid?'

" 'Deed it does,' says the neighbor, 'fer a fact.'

"Well, at that the barker jest had ter get up en go, biddin' 'em a short good-bye so as not ter bust right in front of 'em. Then, turnin' the corner o' the house he jams his hand in his pocket en produces a well-cooked black rock, which fer no reason at all he throws at a perfectly harmless-lookin' dog a-passin' by him.''

WAYNE'S COURTSHIP

"Your turn, Ted."

"Aw, shoot: I don't remember any yarns. Some o' you other fellers tell something."

"Well, sing a song, then."

"Say, I sing about as good as a kettle a-boilin', only when I get through they don't no good come of it."

"Dance, then."

"Say, how can you expect a feller to dance before he's had a shot o' something ter make him feel like it?"

"Looker here, cowboy," said the foreman, getting to his feet, "if you don't want a dose o' the leggin's, you jest better get up on your hind legs en come through."

"Aw, all right fellers, I'll do my little best. Let's see. Some o' you fellers remember old Wayne who used to work fer the Turkey Tracks?"

"Yep, replied several of the boys sitting round the chuck-wagon.

"Well, last fall after we broke up the round-up here I went back to Texas to see my folks, en I run across Wayne. Say, move over en get off my foot. How do yer except me to tell a story with you a-settin' on it?"

"When ridin' through the brush on lower Dev-il's River on my way home, I come on a little clearin' o' some forty acres, en out o' the trail which entered the clearin' from the south side come a man ridin' a bronc that was a-pitchin' ample. Every jump the horse made, the rider was a-handin' him the quoit on either shoulder en a-rakin' him with the spurs, while to help on the show the buster would holler whenever the bronc hit the ground. As I rode out into the clearin', the horse quit pitchin', en I reckonized old Wayne, the same Wayne you fellers know.

"Well, the last time I'd seen Wayne was when he en Slick Mills en Nigger Punch were hazin' a bunch o' stolen cattle up past Red Lake, makin' fer the Pino Wells country, Wayne wasn't so bad, but like lots of others he'd been trailin' with the wrong bunch. Well, after chewin' the rag awhile, we went over to his horse-camp a short distance away, en got us some dinner, Wayne all the time askin' about New Mexico, en how the land lay up there concernin' the trouble he en the others had got into. He had left Lincoln County jest ahead o' the sheriff, who followed him en lost the trail in the foot-hills o' the Capitan Mountains. It was an easy thing in those days, if a man knew the country, to ride the whole length or width o' New Mexico en never hit a ranch, en none knew that better than Wayne en his pardners, which was one reason they ran as long as they did before havin' to quit the country.

"Well, since gettin' back to Texas where his kinfolks lived, Wayne had been goin' straight, breakin' horses en workin' cattle fer his brother en brother-in-law who weren't wise to what Wayne had been doin' over the line.

"Well, I stayed with him that afternoon, helpin'

him ride out a couple o' young horses he had staked, each of which had been ridden jest one saddle before. That night we set up late talkin' over old times, en when we'd had breakfast the next mornin' he asked me to go on into the ranch with him en help move the camp en horses over, en maybe I could get a job with a neighbor that he called old man Tolliver, who had a bunch o' young horses he wanted broke out.

"We got into the ranch late that evenin', en after unpackin' en unsaddlin', turned the stock into the horse pasture en went on over to the house where I met Wayne's brother Doc, his wife ,two kids, en a school marm. The latter Doc had imported, brought over a hundred miles from San Antone, to teach his kids, as there was no local school in the country. Doc who'd never had a chance to go to school himself but was pretty well fixed, had been bound to give his children a good education.   Doc's ranch-house, which was built of logs, contained four large rooms with a gallery on three sides, en a small lean-to kitchen. This had a window without any glass in it, but a wooden shutter about two feet square instead, en at night it was kept closed by an old-fashiend wooden button. The kitchen had a cookin' range, table, cupboard, en a couple of chairs. I'm tryin' to explain the lay of this kitchen, as it was there the event happened which caused Bob to have to take the long trip in the buckboard back to San Antone with the school-marm.

"The ranch, like thousands of other cow ranches in Texas, had only a small piece of land with a title to it. This covered the water and some bottom lands fer hay en plantin' purposes, while the rest was known as free range en was controlled by the ownership o' the water adjoinin' it. Wayne had come back from one of his yearly disappearances about two months before I showed up there. He popped up about the time Christine—that was the name o' the school-marm—arrived from San Antone.

"She was one o' them girls brought up in a city with quite an idea of her own importance, yer know, inclined to believe a man should propose to her before makin' any other advances. Very pretty, en she had somehow safely arrived at the interestin' age o' twenty. Wayne saw through her veneer right off en hurriedly begun to make violent love, in fact proposin' to her on the second night after her arrival, which piece of information Christine imparted to Mrs. Doc as soon as she got the chance. Well, Mrs. Doc, not knowin' what to think of it but hopin' Wayne was sincere, told Christine what a fine feller he was, thinkin' that marriage might tend to settle him down.

"Now Christine—wishin' to assist Mrs. Doc, who had a small child to take care of, offered to wash the dishes after meals, en Wayne gallantly come up to scratch en offered to dry 'em. This arrangement threw 'em together en away from the rest o' the household, as the sink was in the small lean-to kitchen. Hardly a night passed while they was together that Wayne didn't propose, tellin'

Christine that life without her was impossible en so on, en she refusin' him in her kind o' severe way.

"This, as I told yer, continued till I came along. Well, that night Christine told him that he had proposed jest fifty-six times, en she hoped he'd quit. Wayne says that he'd give her jest four more chances that if she didn't accept him after he'd proposed sixty times, he'd do somethin' desperate, but he was bound to have her.

"Well, the night o' the sixtieth arrives, en that evenin' Wayne picks up all the used six-shooter shells he could find around the corrals, puttin' 'em in his left pant's pocket, en a handful o' good cartridges in his right. After supper Christine and he adjourns to the kitchen to wash up the supper dishes, en *she* recollectin' what Wayne had said about him doin' somethin' desperate if she refused him the sixtieth time, she, with a woman's curiosity wonders what it might be.

"They had jest finished with the dishes, she standin' under the open shuttered window, en Wayne between her and the door, when he again proposes, en she refuses him. Well, Wayne lifts the lid off the stove, blazin' with a hot fire, en divin' his hands into his pockets pulls out in the right a handful o' cartridges. 'All right,' he says, 'we will both die together,' en as she turns to jump through the window, he puts the used cartridges he held in his left hand into the stove, shovin' the good ones back in his pocket, en shootin' a couple o' shots from his six-shooter through the roof, ter help things along.

"Well, Wayne noticed when she disappeared through the window that her clothes caught on the wooden window-button, en Mrs. Doc afterwards told him that when Christine got to her room all she had on was her B. V. D.'s. En that's why Doc had to make the hundred-mile drive to San Antone in the buckboard en was short jest one school marm."

Printed in the United States
87617LV00004B/228/A